Her "job" meant acting as the boss's woman

Abby froze in shock as she opened the door. There was a man in her bathroom—a tall wet figure in a terry robe. Kell Balclair, her boss!

"I'm sorry. ... Oh!" she babbled in confusion, turning to flee. Then her heel caught in the folds of her negligee, and she automatically grabbed for support, catching a handful of his robe.

"Now, Abby, don't apologize," Kell said blandly, slipping his arms around her. "Didn't you know we'd be sharing a suite?"

Abby gazed up at him. "It's a wonder you don't expect me to share your bed as well!" she accused.

His firm mouth flickered. "Hmm...a tantalizing idea! I hadn't realized how lovely my new secretary would look with her hair down...."

MARGERY HILTON
is also the author of these
Harlequin Romances

and these
Harlequin Presents

Many of these titles are available at your local bookseller.

For a free catalogue listing all available Harlequin Romances and Harlequin Presents, send your name and address to:

HARLEQUIN READER SERVICE,
1440 South Priest Drive, Tempe, AZ 85281
Canadian address: Stratford, Ontario N5A 6W2

Way of a Man

by

MARGERY HILTON

Harlequin Books

TORONTO • LONDON • LOS ANGELES • AMSTERDAM
SYDNEY • HAMBURG • PARIS • STOCKHOLM • ATHENS • TOKYO

Original hardcover edition published in 1981
by Mills & Boon Limited

ISBN 0-373-02473-8

Harlequin edition published May 1982

CHAPTER ONE

THE flat was like a pigsty as usual!

Abigail Lynwood forgot her pleasant little daydream of Mr Drew and gave a groan of self-righteous disgust. It wasn't fair! When it was her day to 'do' the flat she always managed to get up half an hour earlier and have a rapid skim round which saved some of the rush with vacuum and duster when she got back in the evening. After all, this was the routine mutually agreed on by the four girls who shared the flat, the idea being that it would always be presentable each evening should any of them wish to entertain, to say nothing of their own personal comfort. As Suzanne had said, four girls in a not very large flat meant discipline—or chaos. It was as simple as that. 'So why can't the others stay in line with the rule?' Abby muttered furiously. She did.

She hung up her jacket and went to frown at the rota pinned on the back of the kitchenette door. It was quite explicit:

Monday and Thursday: Abby.
Tuesday and Friday: Emma.
Wednesday and Saturday: Dorice.
Sunday: Suzanne.

Suzanne, who was also Abby's older cousin, escaped one day's chores because she managed the budget side and the paying of bills as her contribution towards the running of the flat. Fair enough, except that the rota didn't work out that way, Abby thought bitterly as she went into the bathroom and surveyed the talcum all over the floor, the sopping towel that had obviously found its way into the bath water at some stage, and the general disarray everywhere. All the hallmarks of Dorice, who would have departed for a modelling session this morning looking as though she had stepped out of a bandbox instead of the untidiest flat in town. And Emma, an aspiring actress, wasn't much better. She always had an involved but watertight excuse for being unable to clear her chores that particular day, with the result that she was continually swapping days with Dorice and the flat betrayed this fact all too clearly.

Abby turned away from the bathroom with a grimace and decided that refreshments were needed first. She made herself a sandwich and a one-teabag pot of tea—an economy drive being in force at the moment—and took the tray through to the sitting room. If the ceilings caved in she wasn't going to shift the mess in that bathroom, it wasn't her turn, but she supposed she would have to restore a little order in the kitchenette, if only because she wanted to eat tonight and tomorrow morning. She munched glumly at the sandwich. She hadn't come to work in wonderful, fabulous London just to end up as the flat skivvy. She'd come to be part of that exciting, cosmopolitan vitality, where there was always something new happening, where fascinating people started new trends and met other fascinating people, where girls met dynamic men and whirled out on the town on a wonderful carousel of gaiety.

Only it hadn't turned out quite like that—yet.

Oh, the carousel whirled gaily enough, and Suzanne and Emma and Dorice seemed to ride it regularly, escorted by exciting males who spoke a language Abby had never learned in the little Northumbrian village where she'd been born and spent her life until three months ago. No, she thought sadly, the carousel never seemed to slow long enough for her to climb aboard. She was still the kid who stood and watched the bright lights swirl and listened to the beat . . .

It wasn't for the want of trying. Since her arrival Abby had worked very hard trying to acquire the London Look, and to an extent she had succeeded quite well. She prided herself that no one would guess that behind the carefully casual grooming there hid a girl from the provinces who was painfully aware that the dream and the reality were two different things. It wasn't *how* one looked, it was having the right kind of personality, like Suzanne, that air of assurance and being witty and amusing. But then Suzanne had always had that glow. Not like me, Abby thought wryly, always able to think of the brilliant retort when everyone had gone home. She could almost hear Grandmother Gabrielle's acid comment, spoken so often in childhood: *'Hm, Suzanne could buy you at one end of the street and sell you at the other, my girl. You'll have to learn to stand up for yourself in this world.'*

And I'm learning—the hard way, Abby told herself flatly. She poured a second cup of the one-bag tea and resolutely pushed away her defeatist train of thought. It was much more pleasant to replace it with a mental picture of Mr Drew.

Mr Drew was the personnel officer at Balclairs, the big pharmaceutical firm in whose office Abby worked as a junior secretary. All the girls were crazy about his blond, playboy looks and magnetic charm, although so far none of them had succeeded in landing a date with him. Abby had secret dreams of being the first to succeed. Instinct told her that her rating would rise to the top of the esteem chart and she would become the most envied girl in the office. For one could aim no higher—except for Mr Kelvyn Balclair himself. He was reputed to be the most divine rake of a man ever created, a bone-melting mixture of Robert Redford, John Travolta, and that gorgeous sexy brute on a Caribbean beach in the new suntan lotion commercial. But as he inhabited more rarefied planes than the little office she shared with four other junior secretaries, and as she had not yet even glimpsed the great man during her six weeks at Balclairs, Abby wisely concentrated her full power of wishful thinking on the more accessible Mr Anthony Drew.

He had come through the juniors' office this afternoon and they had almost swooned at the sight of his tall, debonair figure. He had been wearing skin-tight grey pants, a purple shirt with silvery stripes, and his blond hair falling in a beguiling ruffle on his handsome brow. He was enough to make any girl swoon.

Of course they had all pretended to type furiously, each determined to impress with their efficiency, but four pairs of eyes kept swivelling towards the door through which he would emerge on his return journey. When that moment arrived he bestowed a smile on all five girls, one which a less susceptible feminine gaze might have assessed as being slightly calculated in its charm, and paused as he came near Abby's desk. There he actually stopped, leaned over, and pinched her cheek.

'Still got those country roses and cream in that complexion, I see,' he teased, with another beguiling smile before he passed on his way.

The roses and cream had turned to an unbecoming beetroot, or so Abby felt, but it had made her day, especially when Celia, the senior junior, hissed, 'Hey, what's going on there?'

A reminiscent smile curved Abby's mouth and made her blue eyes dreamy as she surrendered to imagination and forgot her rage at the squalid state of her surroundings. Perhaps she had attracted him at last! Would he single her out again next time? What if he actually asked her out to lunch, or dinner, or to a film ... or a drive out into the country in that stunning scarlet sports car of his. If only Northumbria were not so far away. She would love to show him the village beauty spot where the silvery stream rippled under the quaint old stone bridge that visiting artists often painted. And the path down through the dell, and the narrow cove where the sea curled in on great white billows, just below the little green hollow where the boys tried to persuade the girls to go courting ... What would it be like to be kissed by Mr Drew ...?

'Dreaming again, Abigail?'

Abby gave a violent start. She had not heard anyone come in.

Emma breezed in, slender and boyish in knee-high boots of rose suede that matched her jerkin, and sloshed milk into the beaker she held. She made a place to sit by the simple method of tipping the chair forward until the magazines, last Sunday's *News of the World*, and a pair of somebody's tights cascaded on to the floor, then she sank down with a sigh and swung her elegant legs to rest over the arm of Abby's chair. For a moment she was silent, then she said casually: 'Doing anything special tonight?'

'If you mean am I going to help you out of this chaos—no!' Abby returned flatly, annoyed again at being so rudely turfed out of her pleasurable little daydream. 'It's your turn, Em, and you know it.'

Emma grinned placatingly and took a gulp of milk.

'I wasn't going to ask you. I've a much more special proposition lined up for you tonight.'

'Such as?' Abby was instantly suspicious, knowing Emma's winsome way of cajolery when she wanted something.

'Remember my mentioning Rand Stephens—the TV producer?'

'How could I forget?' Abby observed dryly, suddenly wandering anew what it must be like to have such a marvellous bone structure as possessed by Emma's vivacious face under its smooth cap of close-cropped black hair. Only the perfection of the shape under the skin enabled one to look so wonderful with so severe a hairstyle. She met Emma's pleading glance. 'Well, what about him?'

'He's got a new script, and he thinks there might be a super part in it for me. He wants to see me tonight.'

'Congratulations!' Abby was genuinely delighted, and instantly ready to volunteer help with the hated chores. For poor Emma had been 'resting' so long she had been forced to take on all kind of odd jobs to tide her over until something turned up. Since Abby's arrival on the scene Emma had baby-sat with a very pampered poodle while its wealthy owner (terrified in case darling Fifi caught rabies) went abroad for a week, chauffeured a visiting actress all over London, taken part in several promotions of varying products, shoved hundreds of bills through letterboxes and spent three solid days addressing a mountain of envelopes for a survey. The previous week's evenings had been spent serving drinks at a somewhat shady club in Soho, but, as Suzanne said, Emma could look after herself.

'Thanks . . .' Emma looked remarkably worried for a girl who had a date with an eminent television producer. 'Unfortunately I've got terribly involved. I might not be able to go.'

'Not go?' Abby stared at Emma's tragic expression. 'But why not?'

'I'm supposed to be somewhere else. Oh, if only I'd known that Rand Stephens was going to phone me this afternoon I wouldn't have taken on this other job!' Emma sprang up and came to straddle the camel stool. She stared imploringly at Abby. 'Will you help me— please, Abby?'

'But how?'

'Take on this other job for me—I'll love you for ever if you will.'

'What job?' Abby frowned, a warning hackle rising on her spine. 'I'm no actress, Em.'

'Oh, you don't need to be!' As though she already scented triumph Emma's dark eyes sparkled. 'It's dead easy—all you have to do is to go out for dinner tonight at the Hawaiian Lei, the new place in——'

'Dinner? Me? At the——' Abby drew back in astonishment. 'What are you talking about, Em?'

'Easy, my love. No need to get in a hassle!' Emma grinned. 'Listen. Jem, my agent, fixed this for me this morning—he often does for some of us—it means at least thirty quid and a super meal for free. Of course Jem takes his commish off that. He has an interest in an escort agency, you see, and if they're short of a girl, as sometimes happens—or a man for that matter—they contact him because he can often suggest somebody at short notice. But Rand didn't ring till four, and when I tried to locate Jem to get off the hook he'd gone off some place and won't be back till morning.' In her rush Emma had not noticed Abby's look of dawning horror. 'It's such a fabulous chance—Rand's such a top name his productions sell all over the world, and if he did like me I'd be made! Oh, please, Abby, say you will!'

Abby was shaking her head. 'Have I got this right? You're being paid to go out to dinner tonight at the Hawaiian Lei? But who with?'

'I dunno.' Emma dismissed this with a shrug. 'Some bloke visiting town who wants company for the evening. I've done it before, it's useful money and a meal thrown in.' She stopped and burst out laughing at the expression on Abby's small shocked face. 'It isn't *that* you innocent! At least, it needn't be. We don't have to sleep with them—that's up to us,' she added with a slightly malicious grin, 'if we care to extend the contract beyond midnight. Actually, I've met some fascinating fellers on this lark.'

'Have you?' said Abby in a small voice.

'Well?' Emma raised fine brows.

'No, I'm sorry, Em, but I couldn't possibly!' Abby got up and began gathering together the things Emma had tipped on to the floor. 'I just couldn't.'

There was a silence, broken only by the sounds of Abby's movements. Then Emma said sadly, 'I was afraid you wouldn't. And Dorice is frying other fish tonight, worse luck. I know she'd have done it like a shot. Oh, God, what am I going to *do*?'

'I don't know.' Abby's voice was sympathetic. She wished she could help Emma, but what she asked was out of the question. What on earth would Suzanne say? She was very conscious of having a certain amount of responsibility for the youthful Abby. Suddenly a wry little giggle quirked Abby's lips; what on earth would Grandmother Gabrielle think?

Emma slumped back into her chair. 'I've really done it now! Telling Rand Stephens I'd meet him at eight when I'm supposed to be at the Inn at that time, asking for a Mr Keighley. How on earth am I going to be in two places at once? Tell me, somebody!' she wailed.

Abby turned. 'Oh, you haven't! You didn't take on both dates, surely?'

Emma closed her eyes despairingly. 'What have I been telling you? Of course I did. I was so sure that Dorice would take on the other thing—she owes me a favour—but I forgot that she was going to a special party tonight. She's not coming back to the flat tonight. Oh, jiminy!' she moaned again. 'Jem will be furious if I let him down. You see, I got a fiver on account from him this morning, I'm so broke! He'll put it round the grapevine that I'm a welsher. And if I don't turn up to meet Rand S. he'll say I'm unreliable and I'll never get another chance like it.'

Abby looked at the downbent dark head. The fine bones at the top of Emma's spine showed at the slender nape, making her look curiously vulnerable, and then there was a tremor of her shoulders and a sound very like a choked-back sob. Abby bit her lip, and went slowly to the fireside, where she could see Emma. Almost unwillingly, yet forced by a welling sympathy, she asked, 'What's it like, being an escort girl?'

Emma looked up. 'Oh, there's nothing to it. You dress your best, try to be as sweet and charming as you can. Defer to them over the meal—I mean, if they want to eat snails or frog-spawn don't look sick. You could do it so easily, Abby. Dance with them if they feel so inclined and laugh at their jokes, even if you heard them years ago. Then you insist they put you in a taxi not a minute later than midnight. I believe this man is from the north, like you, and you're a country girl. You'd probably get on a like a couple of fires.' Emma gave a hopeful little smile, her eyes pleading.

'Would we?' There was no conviction in Abby's voice, and doubt still mapped its way over her tense features. Yet she could not bring herself to make the outright refusal that every instinct urged her to cry out before she took on something she might bitterly regret.

'Of course, but forget it. I shouldn't have asked it, not from a nice little kid like you. It isn't fair.' Emma got to her feet, her slender shoulders still drooping, and forced a smile. 'Thanks for being so concerned. You're a good little soul. I hope life doesn't spoil you.'

She turned away, and suddenly Abby came to a decision. She cried, 'No—wait!' and when Emma swung back to face her she gulped. 'I just want to be absolutely sure of one thing . . . If I did, are you certain I—it's not like I've heard . . .? I wouldn't have to . . .?'

'Oh, honey!' Emma began to laugh. 'No! It's exactly as I've told you. All you have to do is keep your head and make sure you're in a taxi for home by midnight. Listen, a man can't seduce you in a crowded restaurant or on a dance floor! If he does make any suggestions about extending the evening just say your name's really Cinderella and you don't think he's cast to play prince tonight. If you have any trouble, and I'm sure you won't, tell him straight you've kept your part of the contract and simply ask the doorman to call you a cab. And that's that!'

For a long moment Abby was silent, then she laughed shakily. 'You must think me very naïve . . .'

Emma shook her head. 'Actually, I think you're very wise. It's easy to get involved in shady assignments if you don't know your way around. Of course some girls'll do anything for money. But do you really mean it? You'll take it on for me?

Abby nodded, and Emma gave a little cry of delight. Throwing her arms round Abby and hugging her exuberantly, she breathed fervently, 'Oh, you're a wonderful angel! I'll do the same for you one day, I promise. Now, what are you going to wear?'

This point had not yet occurred to Abby. However, Emma had an extensive wardrobe geared to all possible occasions, and as the two girls were of the same height and size the dressing of Abby for the ball—as Emma termed it—presented no problems. Half an hour later she was arrayed in a deceptively simple creation of rose silk jersey that clung and flowed in all the right places. It made Abby look in the mirror and gasp slightly, wondering if the reflection there was really her own. Perhaps it was as well that Abby couldn't see just how revealing was the deep horseshoe scoop at the back which dipped deep to the hollow of her spine.

'It looks far better on you than it does on me—you've got a gorgeous shape up front,' observed Emma, with a somewhat envious survey of Abby's voluptuously swathed young bosom. 'Lucky you! I've got to resort to padded bras with bits of cotton wool stuck in the strategic places—and don't let anybody ever kid you that men find flat chests attractive. I know!' added Emma darkly.

Abby blushed, and folded her arms selfconsciously across her chest. She was not used to having her more personal assets discussed so frankly—what would Grandmother Gabrielle say?—and this made Emma start to giggle helplessly.

'Oh, Abby—you're priceless, but don't ever change. One day some heavenly man is going to fall for your innocence like a load of bricks and spend nights of bliss teaching you what it's all about.'

'I think I know what it's all about already,' said

Abby coolly, 'Now hadn't we better get a move on?'

'Yes.' Emma stepped back and gave another long critical stare at the vision in front of her and nodded. 'Couldn't be better. And remember in future when you buy clothes for yourself, avoid the fussy frills and bits and pieces—they usually disguise poor cut or skimpiness in a garment.'

Abby nodded, secretly hoping she was going to be able to sit down gracefully without disarranging those figure clinging lines. At first Emma had wanted her to wear a scarlet panne velvet gown which admittedly suited Abby's colouring divinely but also revealed even more creamy skin both back and front than did the rose silk, so that Abby panicked at the thought of exhibiting herself in it in public. She would certainly look like what Grandmother Gabrielle termed a 'fast creature', and apart from that she was terrified in case she clumsily spilt wine or something over it.

She looked again at the new Abby, secretly pleased with the new hair-style contrived by Emma and the subtle but attractive make-up applied by the same skilful fingers. The silver-rose nail lacquer tipped her slender hands like pearls, and Emma's latest perfume discovery floated in a delicious cloud about her. If only she had the aplomb of an actress to carry the whole thing off . . . She said wistfully, 'I'm beginning to feel like Cinderella.'

'Good—your coach has arrived.' Emma turned from a glance through the window. 'Got everything? Come on, I'll see you off.'

It was not until Abby was sitting in the taxi, Emma's fervent thanks and 'Good luck,' echoing in her ears, that the tremors started. What had she let herself in for? Borrowed finery, dinner at one of the newest and most swish nighteries in town, and what they used to call in her home village a blind date . . .

Supposing he was awful? What if she couldn't think of a thing to say?

The tremors became panic and Abby was possessed of a wild urge to tell the cab driver to turn round and take her back to the flat. Even doing the chores didn't seem so bad now! She was actually leaning forward, her hand raised to tap on the glass, then she sank back against the leather. She had promised Emma; she couldn't go back on her word now.

The cab wound its way across town and reached its destination. It stopped and Abby got out, aghast at the shakiness of her legs. She paid the driver and turned uncertainly towards the hotel entrance, trying to look as though she walked into places like the Inn every day of her life. Nonchalant, blasé, soignée, assured, nodding graciously to the doorman who opened her cab door . . . not Cinderella in a borrowed gown!

Two men leaving the hotel gave her admiring glances that needed little encouragement to become smiles. She returned the glances with a haughty stare and swept past them, then bit her lip; what if one of them turned out to be the man she was supposed to meet? And what if he wasn't there and she had to hang about by herself, with people looking at her . . .?

But it was much easier than she feared. It was exactly eight o'clock, and the first man she glimpsed as she entered and paused hesitantly, looking for reception, came forward.

He said, 'Excuse me . . . are you Miss St Clair?'

She stared at the burly, middle-aged man with the strong, florid colouring in a weatherbeaten face, and instinctively a negative sprang to her lips. Then she remembered Emma's instructions—of course she had to answer to Emma's name. She said, 'Yes, are you . . .?'

'Jack Keighley. Pleased to meet you, Miss St Clair.'

She took the hand he held out, the first warning instinct arising to say that she wasn't going to like this man. Then fairness prompted the mental rebuke that it wasn't always fair to judge by appearances or first impressions. She said awkwardly, 'I didn't expect to find you straight away.'

'Jack Keighley never keeps a lady waiting! Now then, would you like a little drink first, or shall we go?'

She wanted to say go, but again she remembered Emma's instructions: the client was paying! She forced a smile. 'Whichever you prefer, Mr Keighley.'

'Call me Jack. I think we'll go and eat, eh?'

She inclined her head, her young features taut with her inward tension, and he took her arm rather possessively as he escorted her from the hotel. In the cab he sat a bit closer to her than was necessary, and Abby's face clouded with unease. He used a very strong smelling hair-dressing or aftershave, and she could sense the bulk of his flesh straining against his clothes. The dimness inside the cab seemed like a wall that shut out the brilliance of the city lights outside and set the scene for an invitation this man would not hesitate to use. She thought desperately, *get him talking*, and asked him how he liked London.

'It's all right. Just a bit more of the same and a bit bigger.' With this somewhat enigmatic pronouncement he slewed round and patted her hand jovially. 'What's the grub like at this new place?'

'I don't know. I haven't been there.'

'That makes two of us, eh? I'd have thought a girl like you would know her way round the lot.'

If only he knew! she thought hysterically.

'But it is the latest "in" place?'

'Oh, yes. The decor is very exotic and there's a miniature lagoon with real fish and tropical plants.' She repeated the description provided by Emma and saw his head nod approvingly.

'Waitresses in grass skirts and not much else?' he asked hopefully. 'Something to tell the lads about when I get back.'

There was a silence, rapidly becoming awkward to Abby, and she said in a strained, bright little voice, 'Are you on holiday?'

'No. Business.'

'Are you having a successful trip?'

'That remains to be seen. But let's not talk about work, lovey, eh?'

Silence came again and Abby's spirits drooped. She wasn't making a very successful escort girl. She was certain she detected puzzlement in her companion and an air of boredom already in the atmosphere. With a rush of relief she glimpsed the green and white neon palms outside the Hawaiian Lei shining ahead, and presently the cab slowed. It would be easier once they were there amid the lights and music and starting the meal.

But it wasn't.

Abby was a genuinely conscientious girl who, once she had committed herself to a promise or a project, considered that any failure which ensued must be due to some extent to her own inadequacy. Not for the eighteen-year-old Abby the excuses and self-justification after something had gone wrong.

Had she been more experienced of male nature she would have realised that Jack Keighley was as much out of his element as she was. Back in his northern home town Jack was a beer and club man, at ease amid the double-edged jokes and ribaldry, and at heart as good-natured as the next. But away from it all and the surveillance of a not unsuspicious wife, Jack Keighley was bent on a good time and a feminine conquest of which he could boast to the lads on his return to the ambiance of clubland. And he was not worried about paying for it.

Poor Abby had no idea at the start of that evening just how hopelessly wrong Emma had been in her surmise; the last thing Jack Keighley wanted was an innocent country girl whose village upbringing had instilled in her a moral code far from the intemperance of the hopes lurking in Jack Keighley's mind.

Abby did her best. She smiled at his sallies. She bore gracefully with the familiarities that became more pronounced as the evening wore on and the influence of alcohol increased his confidence and bonhomie. But he drank too much, talked too loud, and laughed too immoderately, and his idea of dancing when they took to the floor was to enclose her in a vice against him and press his hot sweaty hand into her bare back.

She hated every moment of it, and but for her promise to Emma she would have run out into the night long before yet another surreptitious glance at her watch told her that midnight was still far distant.

When they had reached the sweet course of their meal a party of four people arrived at the next table. The older man and woman sounded like Americans, as did the young woman, who was extremely attractive in a brittle kind of way and obviously knew it. But the other man caught Abby's wayward interest. He was tall, with rugged good looks and a hard lean jawline that with the firm set of his mouth and alert eyes suggested a forceful character. The girl appeared to be very keen on him, sending him meaning glances and sometimes putting her hand on his arm and leaning her head confidentially towards him, once so close that her red-gold hair touched his thick, dark brown ruffled head.

Abby started weaving a foolish little fantasy; that she sat where the titian-haired enchantress held sway, hearing the voice of that intriguing-looking man— surely he'd have a warm, rich tone to caress the listening ear—and seeing those fascinating creases deepen in his cheeks when he smiled . . .

'. . . and fill the lady's glass as well.'

Jack Keighley's slightly slurred tones brought Abby back to reality, just in time to place her hand firmly over the top of the wine-glass the waiter was about to replenish.

'Now don't be silly!' Keighley's big hand tried to grasp hers to force it away, and as she resisted the glass went over, spilling the rosé into an accusing spread of pink across the snowy cloth.

Abby wished she could die on the spot. With a deft movement the waiter covered the stain with a clean napkin and gave a reassuring murmur to the scarlet-cheeked Abby. Her companion's voice was raised, ordering another glass to be brought, which was already being done, and the party at the next table looked across with what seemed to Abby to be expressions of total disgust. Looking up, she encountered the cold grey glance of the dark man, and read scorn in its depths. Her mouth quivered, but her small chin lifted; he had no right to look at her like that and misjudge . . .

She forced herself to ignore the stranger, to try to be amusing and appear amused, while the minutes ticked by with agonising slowness. She danced again with her

lumbering partner, suffered his hot hands and his
spirit-laden breath, listened to his inanities when they
went on to the palm-thatched balcony where the bar
overlooked the miniature lagoon, and at last the
pointers on her watch stood at five to twelve.

She took a deep breath and said unsteadily, 'I think
it's time to leave, Mr Keighley. It's nearly midnight.'

'Flower! I thought you'd never say the word!' A grin
spread over his face and he staggered a little, catching
at her arm as he clumsily regained his balance. 'Do
you want one for the road?'

'No, thank you.' She disengaged her arm and forced
a smile. 'I'll just get my wrap.'

She hurried away, a great thankfulness in her heart
that the ordeal was over at last. In a quarter of an
hour, with luck, she'd be safe home, telling Emma all
about it and hearing news from Emma that she hoped
would make it all worthwhile. All she had to do was
say goodnight; if she knew where the staff entrance
was she'd be tempted to run the gauntlet of startled
waiters and escape that way . . .

Jack Keighley was planted solidly at the foot of the
stairs. He watched her descend and stepped forward.
'Now, love. Your place? Or back to the hotel?'

'What?' Abby's eyes widened. 'But it's midnight.
I——'

'So what?' He put his arm round her waist, pulling her to his side. 'The night's young. We're going
to——'

'No!' Aware of turning heads, she tried to draw away
and lowered her voice. 'You know very well, Mr
Keighley, the evening's over, the contract was only
for——'

'Now don't be coy, flower——I know all about that,
so don't worry. It's strictly between ourselves after

midnight. So let's see your pretty little smile again—
I'm a generous man, I'll see you all right, love.'
Suddenly his arm reached for her again and he rubbed
his hand up and down her hip while he tried clumsily
to nuzzle her ear.

'Stop—how dare you!' Heedless of making a scene,
she broke free and darted towards the glass doors that
led into the outer lobby. Her one thought was escape
as she pushed blindly through a group of people in her
path.

But Jack Keighley was not too drunk to think and
move swiftly. He caught up with her by the doors and
seized her shoulder. 'Just a minute! If you think you're
going to run out on me like this, my girl, after——'

'Please——let me go!' Tears of humiliation misted
Abby's eyes as she tried to fight free of Jack Keighley's
belligerent grip. And then a dark form loomed in front
of her.

'Do you need help? Or is this a lovers' tiff?'

Abby blinked and saw the stranger from the next
table, ice in his eyes and distaste tightening his mouth
as he looked from Abby's distraught face to her companion's angry glare.

'Oh yes, please! He——'

'Now wait a minute!' Keighley bellowed. 'You keep
out of this! I've paid thirty quid for——'

'No!' Abby broke in, and clutched at the stranger's
arm. 'It was just for the evening—till midnight! And
now he wants——'

'Is there some trouble?' A large man in dinner dress
had materialised silently, and now stood before them,
wearing the cold, wary expression of one who has seen
it all before.

'Nothing we can't take care of.' The tall stranger
turned to Abby, glancing down at the small desperate

fingers still clutching at his sleeve as though at a life-line. 'Escort girl?'

'No!' Then she remembered and nodded miserably. 'But it's true—you can check up if you don't believe me.' She gave him the name of the agency Emma had mentioned, praying that Emma had been completely honest with her.

The big man who looked like the manager nodded, and the tall stranger said to him curtly, 'See that this—gentleman—gets a cab. And make my excuses to my party. Table nineteen. I'll rejoin them as soon as I can.'

He seized Abby's arm with fingers that felt like steel vices, and she was hurried out of the entrance before she quite knew what was happening. Fresh cool night air met her heated face and she was vaguely aware of the protesting voice of Jack Keighley being cut off as the heavy glass doors swung shut behind her.

But the grip of the stranger did not slacken. He stalked along the dark pavement, steering her firmly, and unlocked the door of a Lancia as rakish and stylish as himself. He gave Abby a none too gentle thrust, and when she shot a scared glance at him over her shoulder he said brusquely: 'Get in and don't argue.'

'But——'

'I said get in—unless you'd prefer to wait for your client to catch up with you.'

Abby got in, casting a desperate prayer heavenwards that an even worse fate did not lie in wait for her, and the stranger slammed the door shut before hurrying round to the driver's side.

'Where do you live?'

Abby found her voice. 'You—you don't need to t-take me home. I can get a cab.'

'I may as well finish the rescue operation.' His tone

was curt and his movements sharp as he started the car and pulled away. 'Left or right?' he snapped as they slid up to the junction.

'Oh—I d-don't know,' stammered poor Abby. 'The taxi came in the other way—it must be a one-way street.'

There was a stifled exclamation that was daunting to say the least. Then, 'Do you know if you live in the north, south, east or west of the city? So that we can make our way in the right direction while you remember precisely where you *do* live.'

In an even smaller voice than before Abby gave him her address, and then a very chill silence permeated the car. It lasted all of the twenty-five minutes it took to reach the road where she lived, and certainly did not invite any efforts at small talk, even if Abby had felt capable of trying. She was conscious only of relief to see the familiar outlines of the tall, converted semi and the friendly glimmer of light at the window of the first floor flat. Someone was still up; probably Emma, waiting anxiously to hear that all had gone well. And how! A grimace of distaste wrinkled Abby's nose and a tremulous sigh escaped her as the car slowed to a halt.

She clutched at her evening purse in preparation for her exit and stole a glance at the profile of her rescuer. Where were the foolish dreams she had woven around him so recently? No dimness of a car interior could conceal the hard, implacable set of the features turning towards her. She licked dry lips.

'It—it was very kind of you to bring me home. I—I don't know how to thank you, Mr . . . Mr . . .'

He ignored the hesitant groping for his name. 'Your client could doubtless have suggested a way,' he said dryly.

'Oh!' Abby recoiled. 'Are you——?' Speechless, she fumbled desperately for the door catch.

'No, you little fool—only that you might have expected that.' He touched a switch and the roof light illuminated Abby's scared little face. 'You're new to it all, aren't you?'

Abby's frayed pride came back to life. She stiffened. 'What do you mean? New to what?'

He gave a short, contemptuous laugh. 'You'll soon learn—if you stay in that business very long.'

There was no mistaking his meaning. Abby forgot the elusive door catch and clenched her fists. 'How dare you suggest that I . . .? It's not true! Do you think I enjoyed that—that beastly man and his horrible paws?' A shudder of revulsion ran through her at the memory. 'It was horrible! I—I can't bear being touched like that. And I——'

'You're going to have to get used to it, aren't you? Or——'

'How dare you insult me? I'm *not*——'

'I'm not insulting you,' he broke in curtly, 'merely stating a fact. Listen, little Miss Innocent Escort Girl. Obviously you haven't yet learned to take the rough with the smooth. Unfortunately, it's necessary where getting easy money is concerned. Oh, forget it,' he added impatiently as fresh horror and anger tautened her face. 'Only remember, next time I won't be around to do the rescue.'

Abby was beginning to feel that she'd lost St George and found the dragon. 'I—I don't know why you bothered, then,' she sobbed, and managed to get the car door open at last. 'I thought you were kind and—and instead you're——'

'Keeping my guests waiting,' he snapped, 'while I'm fool enough to feel sorry for a silly little girl who looks as though she ought to be tucked up with her teddy bear instead of out on the streets of London!'

Abby almost fell out of the car in her haste. She was rapidly forgetting gratitude. She turned to shut the car door, and saw her gallant knight leaning across the passenger seat to deliver a parting broadside.

'Forget about the glitter—it's dross! Take my advice,' he rapped, 'find yourself a steady job in an office or a dress shop or something. Goodnight!'

While Abby gaped at him he reached over and slammed the door out of her grasp. The car engine roared into powerful life and the red tail lights swept away into the darkness, leaving her standing on the kerb, trembling with anger and hurt and humiliation.

At last she turned and let herself blindly into the house, to pour out the story and seek sympathy from Emma. 'Promise you won't tell Suzanne,' she begged fearfully. 'She'd be mad!'

'Not a hope!' Emma assured her fervently, well aware that her own standing would not be enhanced if the escapade came out. She stirred vigorously at the hot milky cocoa and steered the still shaken Abby towards bed. 'I'm terribly sorry to have landed you with such a beastly time, my pet. I never thought . . . the agency really does have rules and it's a very reputable one. Now you drink that and forget all about it.'

But it was easier said than done.

Abby drank the comforting beverage and then settled down to sleep, miserably aware that her last glimpse of the stranger's scornful face was going to stay indelibly printed on her mind for a long time to come.

CHAPTER TWO

By the following weekend Abby had almost succeeded in relegating that unpleasant experience to where it belonged—firmly in the past. But every so often the memory of the stranger would rap on her mind's door, demanding admission and invariably bringing a flush of mingled shame and anger to her cheeks. It was so unfair. He had thought the worst of her, when all she had done was try to do someone a good turn. Tucked up with her teddy bear, indeed! After coming to her rescue like a masterful hero of old and sweeping her out of a very embarrassing situation he had heaped scornful advice and undisguised disgust on her innocent head, refusing to give her a chance to explain until she was so furious she wouldn't even try.

Abby took refuge in the whimsy of how it should have been. Why couldn't he behave like a true knight? Courteous and gallant, vowing he could not bear to leave her to the lecherous mercies of Mr Keighley, and when he brought her home handing her out of the car, tenderly escorting her to the safety of her door and pressing her hand to his lips as he bade her goodnight. *Oh, go away!* she muttered furiously as the misty dream picture grinned sardonically. It was just like looking at a bright object and still seeing it when one shut one's eyes, until the dazzly effect went off. *You're a fool, Abigail Lynwood,* she told herself. *Go find your sense of humour again and get on with life.*

It was sensible advice to herself, but unfortunately it proved such a dull week, marked only by one of her grandmother's rare telephone calls on the Thursday evening. It seemed that their neighbour at the farm was making a visit to London at the weekend to visit her mother who had recently come out of hospital after a serious illness.

'And Meg's taking the children,' said Grandmother Gabrielle. 'I know her mother wants to see them, but I reckon she'll need another rest-cure after a weekend of those kids' undiluted company, and cooped up in a flat. So I wondered . . . I haven't mentioned it to Meg yet in case you're busy . . . perhaps you and Suzanne might take them off her hands in the afternoon, give her a chance to talk to her mother in peace? But of course I realise it's short notice to give you.'

'I don't know about Suzanne,' said Abby, 'but I'm not doing anything special. I'll take them to the Zoo.'

Suzanne, when she came home later that evening, shuddered at the mere thought and said she couldn't possibly change her plans for the weekend. So Abby, aided by Emma, who was still resting, took Pete and Mandy to the Zoo on the Saturday afternoon, and spent a somewhat lurid Sunday between Madame Tussaud's and laser rock at the Planetarium, after which the two girls felt anything but rested and the children were just getting warmed up.

'Can we go to the Zoo again—it's not far away,' asked Mandy, pointing a sticky finger infallibly in the direction of Regent's Park.

Emma raised fine brows. 'Nothing wrong with their sense of direction!'

'I want to go on the Underground—down the deep ones with the biggest escalators,' said Pete. 'Come on— there's a station.' He also extended a grubby but determined finger at the sign almost overhead.

'Why not?' Emma grinned. 'I haven't played on the

Underground since I came to London when I was nine. Do you know if the Bank's open on Sundays—they'd love the moving thingummy there.'

Abby didn't know, and she couldn't raise a great deal of enthusiasm for either suggestion. Her hair felt untidy, she was hot and sticky, and the icecream Pete had inadvertently dropped down her skirt earlier in the day had now dried to horrid smudges. She was beginning to feel that they had done their duty as far as entertaining Meg's two demanding young handfuls went. But Pete's large blue eyes were eloquent. She relented. 'All right, just for half an hour, then we'll have tea somewhere and then we'll have to take you home.'

'Oh, goody!' Pete whooped, turning to make a dive towards the tube entrance and colliding full tilt with a tall man hurrying from the opposite direction.

The tall man in the pale grey suit recoiled, then steadied young Pete and looked over the boy's head straight into Abby's startled gaze. Recognition was instant and mutual. The stranger's expression grew sardonic.

'A very young client this time,' he observed. His glance flickered to Emma, whose cool, arresting attractiveness was as unflurried as ever, and lingered there appreciatively for a moment before returning to Abby. His brows went up. 'Or is it Aunties Anonymous at weekends?'

Before Abby could recover her voice and urge Pete into apologising the stranger had moved on. She stared after his tall, immaculate figure, until Emma exclaimed, 'Well! And what was all that about?'

Abby told her, and was not amused by Emma's amusement. 'But look at me! I'm a sight!' she wailed.

'Icecream down my skirt and my hair a mess!'

'So what?' Emma grinned. 'He's a callous, cruel brute—you told me so yourself. So what does it matter what he thinks about your appearance?' She paused, her eyes becoming thoughtful. 'I must say I never imagined he was like that. You chose a right stunner to be rescued by.'

'Aunty Gail——' Pete was tugging at Abby's hand, '——I'm sorry about the icecream—I thought I rubbed it all off with my hankie.'

'Rubbed it all in, you mean, you rip,' Emma giggled.

'I had no choice about it,' Abby said tartly to Emma as she put her arm round the woebegone Pete, who seemed to think it was all his fault. 'Yes, I know you rubbed it all off, pet. Come on, we'll go on the Underground.'

Aware of the grin still playing mischievously on Emma's face, she hurried after the two children. So Emma thought he was a stunner! Well, she had thought that when she first set eyes on him during that ghastly evening with the irresponsible Emma's client. But he'd soon demolished her foolish fancies. And why hadn't that cool, logical little fact Emma had mentioned registered the moment he loomed up out of nowhere? He'd made no secret of his opinion of a silly, flighty little idiot whose morals were extremely suspect, and had no hesitation in pinning that opinion on the character of one Abigail Lynwood, on the strength of one very unfortunate encounter. So what the devil did it matter what he thought of her appearance? Aunties Anonymous indeed!

Abby smarted every time she remembered that second brief encounter. Now it was going to take another week before time settled her ruffled feelings. Of all the lousy luck; even London wasn't big enough to prevent a collision like that!

She took to looking cautiously ahead of her during the next few days and staring fixedly out of the windows on the bus in case he should get on—until it occurred to her to that the owner of the car in which she'd been brought home was not likely to be dashing for the 22 bus at rush hour, nor rushing anywhere at all. He looked the type of man to whom others would rush instantly at his behest and act on his commands. The thought made Abby shudder; how awful to be at the mercy of such a tyrant, simply because one had to live and fate had cast him at the apex of the pyramid and yourself among the slaves at the bottom of the heap. No wonder there were revolutions!

However, she was able to console herself with the thought that it had all been worthwhile when Emma whooped into the flat the following Tuesday with the news that she was to go to a script reading for Rand's new production and if the casting director liked her she was in!

They had an advance celebration that night, and Abby was still almost as excited as Emma when she set off for the office next morning. At last she had something to tell the other girls, even if it were only reflected glory that depended on several more of those all important 'ifs'. If Emma got the part, if the play was a success, if Emma became a star . . .

But there was a message waiting for her that banished all thought of Emma's fate from her mind; Mr Drew wanted to see her as soon as she got in. Abby hastily checked her appearance and the time—it was nearly nine-fifteen already, but she'd missed her usual bus—and hurried anxiously to Mr Drew's office. What had she done? It couldn't be the sack! Prepared for the worst, she tapped on the panel under the neat-lettered sign that said: Mr Anthony Drew, Personnel Manager, and obeyed the crisp, 'Come,' that sounded in response.

She walked in, taking no pleasure from that brief, beguiling smile of acknowledgment which as a rule could set her heart a flutter. 'You wanted to see me?' she said in a slightly strained voice. 'I'm sorry I'm a bit late, but I missed——'

'You won't have to miss anything in future now.' He waved towards the chair before the desk. 'Sit down, Miss Lynwood.'

She missed the conditional 'now' in her relief that he seemed uncaring of her lack of punctuality. He shuffled some papers together and pushed them aside, reaching for a buff-coloured folder before he looked up and regarded her with shrewd eyes that did not miss the nervously tensed movement of the slim hands clasped on her lap.

'How would you like to be promoted?' he asked at last.

'Promotion?' Her eyes widened. Instantly a glorious vista of her own little office and a comforting bulge in her bank statement floated in her mind. Where would it be? More important—to whom?

'You know, of course, that Balclairs are in the process of removing, lock, stock and barrel, out of town?' Mr Drew said in jocular tones.

Abby did know. There had been mixed feelings among her colleagues. All of them grumbled about the cost of living incurred by working in the City, yet none of them seemed very enthusiastic about uprooting themselves for the wilds of Surrey, where the new manufacturing plant had been set up. The adjoining office block was virtually complete and already Sales and Admin had made the transfer. Only a skeleton staff remained in the old office and soon Balclairs would grace the City no longer. It was rumoured that they had cleared a cool twelve million when they disposed of the original century-and-a-half-old factory, and confidently expected to clear another bomb when they finally vacated the present office site. You reckoned ground by the inch when selling in central London these days.

'I expect the grapevine has kept you pretty well in the picture regarding the great move,' Mr Drew broke in on her thoughts, 'so I won't waste time on the whys and wherefores. Are you ready for Surrey?'

Abby looked uncertain. 'You—you said promotion, Mr Drew.'

'I did. You're going on a month's trial. Secretary to—guess who?'

For a wild moment she thought he referred to himself and a sparkle of incredulous hope and disbelief glowed in her eyes. 'You mean——?'

'Yes, none other—K.B. himself. Aren't you a lucky girl?'

'What!' Abby gaped. She could not help it. K.B. Mr Balclair! *The Chief!*

Mr Drew appeared amused by her astonishment. 'Only on trial, you understand. You'll have to prove yourself.'

'Yes—but I've only been here seven weeks,' was all she could say, while her mind got to grips with this bombshell. Golly! Secretary to the Chief himself! After only seven weeks with the firm and scarcely three months as a career girl in town.

'We're aware of that,' Mr Drew replied, a trace of irony in his tone. 'Unfortunately, the girl in line for the job has just landed an executive post abroad. And

K.B.'s own secretary is leaving at the end of the month to get married.' Mr Drew leaned back and studied Abby's excited face with shrewd eyes. 'You probably know that our policy is to promote as far as possible within our own staff, and the Chief has his own ideas in the matter.' He paused, and the echoes of K.B.'s terse instructions floated back. *'For heaven's sake, send me a girl who can spell and who'll take a telling. Not one of the flighty chits who keeps her make-up kit and pills in the stationery drawer, and not one of the old pussies who'll tell me what to do. On second thoughts—send me somebody young and malleable.'* Well, this one seemed malleable enough, Mr Drew reflected silently.

Abby bit her lip nervously. She was beginning to remember overheard snippets about K.B. Not just the bits about his personal appearance and the sex appeal he could exude when the fit took him, but the rather more daunting rumours of ruthlessness, impatience, slave-driving, and a marked histrionic tendency to play God in emergencies . . .

'What's he like?' Abby asked warily.

'Okay, and fair enough—as long as one does the job properly. But I'll warn you, he doesn't suffer fools gladly.' Suddenly Anthony Drew's grin flashed. 'You're not scared, are you? Don't you trust my powers of judgment?'

'Yes, of course,' Abby said quickly, though inwardly she was beginning to have doubts.

'You'd better! Remember, this is my job, slotting people in and sorting out the problems. I don't make mistakes—I'd soon be out on my neck if I did. Now, I'll brief you . . .'

Abby was starting to feel that she'd boarded the carousel at last—at full speed. She was to begin her new post the following week, so that Carola could initiate her successor into the routine before she departed on the wedding march. Mr Drew suggested that Abby should commute to Lingwood during the trial month.

'You shouldn't have much trouble with transport. Quite a few of the staff were pleasantly chuffed to find those jam-packed trains going out half empty in the morning and reversing the process at the evening rush hour. Then, if you settle in to K.B.'s satisfaction, we'll help you to find accommodation if you have any problems. It's a pleasant spot, relaxing, out of the rat race. Although I hope it doesn't prove too relaxing! Racing with the rats keeps one up to scratch!'

He snapped her file shut and sent it skidding across his desk, leaning back and surveying her with a trace of finality. Obviously the interview was over· 'Well?' he said, when she did not speak. 'Any questions?'

Abby could not think of a thing, but she knew this blank would be remedied the moment she was outside the door. She murmured, 'Thank you, Mr Drew,' and he swung to his feet, coming round the desk to touch her cheek with a friendly gesture and give her a special smile.

'Good luck,' he said jocularly, and actually opened the door for her. Abby found herself outside, still feeling somewhat dazed.

Next week . . .

The rest of the week passed all too quickly. When the surprise wore off Abby was beset by doubts of her own ability. This was her third job, and none of them seemed to have provided her with the kind of experience possessed by that worldly, self-assured breed of London secretaries to august personages such as managing directors. When she had completed her course at a northern college she had found a position without any difficulty at a timber merchants just outside her own home town. It was a friendly place, not too large, and her duties were somewhat varied. The owner, an elderly man, found her a willing apprentice, and she soon learned to cope with invoices, keep the V.A.T. books in order and deal with the correspondence. No one said anything if she rearranged her work times in order to collect shopping for her grandmother, and she got used to making the morning mugs of tea for the lads in the timber yard who chaffed and teased her and sometimes took her out—most of them she had known since schooldays—and she did not mind in the least when her boss's daughter left her poodle and toddler son in Abby's charge while she went to the hairdresser each week.

It was all very informal, and Abby soon worked out a competent routine, as well as learning quite a lot about grades and sizes of timber, but after about six months she began to feel restless. There seemed nothing new to discover, and she had a vision of herself ten years older, still looking out at those great stacks of pinky-yellow wood and hearing the whine of the saw. Her shorthand was never needed, after the first couple of weeks Mr Wade tended to tell her what he wanted to say and then disappear across the yard leaving her to get on with it, and the funny, ramshackle little office hut had never known a typewriter of a younger vintage than circa 1920, let alone refinements like dictaphones or filing cabinets. Then Suzanne came home to be bridesmaid at a school friend's wedding.

She breezed in, wearing the aura of a sophisticated career girl and the kind of make-up and gear that made the local matrons frown at the way the elder Lynwood girl had turned out since she left home.

Abby heard all about the new ballet at the Garden, the terrific party Suzanne had been to the night before she left, and the marvellous man she'd just met who was taking her to Paris with him in three weeks' time. Abby was sworn to secrecy about this, of course, and Abby had to admit that her sympathies were with her cousin; Suzanne's mother was a domineering woman, and as Abby grew older she had often breathed a prayer of thankfulness that it was Grandmother Gabrielle who had taken over the care of her after the tragic loss of Abby's parents in a continental coach accident when Abby was only seven.

She'd had a long talk with her grandparents and Suzanne before Suzanne left on the Sunday, and some six weeks later Abby found herself at last in the big, wonderful city, settled in the flat with Suzanne and Emma and Dorice, but anything but settled in her first job there. The pleasant woman who had interviewed Abby wasn't at that branch and the middle-aged woman to whom Abby was assigned proved acid and distinctly unwelcoming, obviously regarding Abby as somewhat wanting merely because she was provincial. Her abruptness made Abby nervous and therefore prone to mistakes she would not have made normally. The building itself was rather dark and overheated and seemed stifling to Abby, fresh from the bracing Northumberland climate. By afternoon she felt heavy-headed and languid, and the general air of discontent that hovered among the rest of the staff did not make for efficiency. It did not take much persuasion from Emma to start Abby on renewed study of the vacancy ads, and when the Balclair ad appeared she instantly had that feeling that it was for her. The first glimpse of Anthony Drew and the happy atmosphere instantly discernible through the building clinched it. She practically begged Mr Drew to give her the job, and almost kissed the letter when its confirmation came.

So here she was, six weeks later, not sure if it was all happening and she was stepping off the train into Kingsley Heath station at eight-thirty of a Monday morning in late September, the plum secretarial job of the company awaiting her.

Trustful of Mr Drew's directions, she turned to her left along a tree-shaded road which brought her to the High Street of the little town. Straight over the crossroads and another five minutes' walk brought her in sight of the new Balclair complex. The sparkling white buildings did not look in the least like a factory, more like a big airy modern school in wide spacious grounds newly lawned and dotted with young tree saplings. The office block lay to the right, with a big half-moon-shaped parking area nearby and a forecourt of tinted flagstones like a terracotta and amber checkerboard leading to the entrance.

The glass doors parted silently as she approached, and inside the spacious lobby a uniformed doorman gave her a cheerful smile. 'You're first this morning, Miss Lynwood—new broom, eh?' he said when she gave her name. 'Don't worry—we all feel like that on the first day!'

Heartened a little by this welcome, despite a certain suggestion of sympathy in his expression, Abby followed his directions and found her way to the quiet opulence of the M.D.'s suite. It was unlocked, except for the inner door, and Abby wandered curiously round the office that would be her domain. The desk was placed in a position just right for the light, and she peeped under the cover to find a superb electric machine—the very latest electronic model. The decor was a cool pastel blue and the carpet a deeper toned blue, the paintwork was white, and the chairs upholstered in a warm dark cerise. Three French

Impressionist prints hung on the walls, unobtrusive yet adding further touches of warmth.

Abby went to the wide window which overlooked the front of the grounds. Cars were rolling up now and people were hurrying across the forecourt below. The suite was well insulated and no sounds penetrated it, but she sensed the scurry and activity beginning to permeate the building. She stood watching for a while, wondering which neatly suited male emerging from a newly arrived car would prove to be the great man himself. That young man in the silvery grey, with the lean, good-looking features and the *Financial Times* in his hand . . . or that tall, broad-shouldered man in the blue, snugly waistcoated suit with distinctive Italian lines . . .

Abby's heart began to palpitate. What if Carola was late and K.B. walked in now, expecting to find his third hand ready to anticipate his every wish? She would feel such a helpless idiot, the very thing he was reputed not to suffer. Feverishly Abby took off her coat and checked her make-up. She would have liked to tidy her hair, but she'd better not go in search of a cloak-room in case K.B. turned up the moment she disappeared.

It was twenty past nine before a tall, raven-haired girl in a scarlet raincoat over a dark blue jersey suit rushed in. She saw Abby standing by the window and exclaimed breathlessly: 'So you got here okay—sorry I'm late, but I had to call in at Marlins to see the bridesmaids' coronets. Don't know why I decided to have a full-scale wedding! There're so many things to see to. I'm Carola, by the way. Won't be a sec.'

The 'sec' stretched into nearly ten minutes before Carola returned, now cool and immaculate and looking every inch the perfect secretary.

'Mr Balclair won't be in today—he's entertaining a party of Belgian chemists,' Carola informed Abby. 'So we can have a peaceful day!'

'Is he as bad as that?'

'Not really, but try not to be late, ever, and always have the current gen ready to hand. He hates to be kept waiting.'

It was all something of an anticlimax, Abby reflected as Carola showed her where everything was kept and explained the routine. The routine seemed to vary considerably—far from a routine, in fact—and there were so many things to remember that Abby's expression grew more and more tense as she tried to store them all up in her brain. But Carola said it was all quite easy and assured her she would have no problems as long as she never allowed herself to get in a flap. The row of technical reference books looked daunting, especially the great fat pharmacopia when she opened its pages, but Carola merely smiled.

'Don't worry about those. The technical department handles all that side of the correspondence, but occasionally it creeps in here and it's as well to be able to check the spelling. Now,' she glanced at her watch, 'I think we'll have early lunch today, then I'll show you around to give you an idea of the layout of the place.'

There was a pleasant canteen, where the food was very good. Carola introduced Abby to several members of the staff as they drifted in to eat, and afterwards took her on the promised tour of the complex. 'The labs are over there.' She pointed to the long blocks that stretched across the western and largest section of the site. 'You won't have cause to go over there, but watch out for Dickie Tennant, our chief technician—and Balclair's big bad wolf. Let him date you at your peril!'

Abby filed yet another name away amid all the other data for future reference as they returned to the office. There, Carola produced a couple of mini tapes and handed them to Abby.

'You may as well get used to the sound of his voice. You'll be hearing quite a lot of it!'

'Does he usually put his letters on tape?' Abby was aware of faint disappointment; her vague mental pictures of herself sitting cool and poised, pen and pad at the ready, the efficient and indispensible third hand to her handsome, dashing king-pin K.B. was a very satisfying one. Sitting transcribing tapes and keeping importunate visitors in their place was not to her liking at all.

'Sometimes,' Carola nodded. 'And masses of memos if he's away and I'm not needed on the trip. He has three of those pocket recorders—and that's another thing—always be sure you reload with a blank tape so that he doesn't take off with an empty machine. That's a sure ticket to fireworks.'

Carola slipped the cassette into the desk recorder and turned away. 'I'll leave you to it—I want to get half a dozen acknowledgments off for wedding presents while I've a spare moment.'

Apart from several telephone calls and a few queries which Carola dealt with, the next hour or so passed without incident. Abby did the tapes, conscious of a certain fascination in the deep, crisp voice they held and a rather peculiar reaction deep within herself, almost as though those cadences played on a tense little nerve somewhere in her being. She pushed away the feeling, telling herself she was being stupid and fanciful, and got on with her work. She transcribed the first tape and submitted the copies for Carola's approval, then started on the second.

A few minutes later Carola stood up.

'Abby, would you mind if I pushed off now? There's not much else to do and I've masses waiting at home.' At the flash of apprehension that crossed Abby's face she laughed. 'Don't worry, I'll tell Switchboard to re-route any important calls through to Mr Gordon—nobody'll bother you with vital decisions and everybody knows K.B. isn't in today.'

Abby nodded, secretly convinced that some vital emergency would crop up the moment Carola left the building and she wouldn't have a clue how to deal with it. From the window she watched the scarlet-rain-coated Carola whisk down the drive and then returned to typing the transcription. When she had finished she checked it carefully, convinced herself that it was perfectly neat and mistake-free, then glanced at her watch. It was still only ten to four; an hour to go, and conscience wouldn't let her follow Carola's footsteps.

She tidied the desk, looked at her watch again—eight and a half minutes to four—and contemplated going to the canteen for a cup of tea. Then she decided not to, something might turn up . . . Almost without realising it, she switched on the recorder and listened to that voice. There was something about it . . . Suddenly there was a rush of feet outside and the door flew open. Abby almost cried out with shock.

A young man with thick fair hair and a lean, whimsical face stood there, staring at her with surprised blue eyes. 'Where's Carola?' he asked.

'She—she's not here at the moment,' said Abby, instinctively biting back the fact that Carola had gone in case trouble should ensue for her. 'Can I help?'

'Are you K.B.'s latest?'

'I'm his new secretary,' Abby said primly, not quite sure of the sound of that 'latest'.

'Ye gods—he's going back to the cradle!' The young man advanced into the room and looked at Abby with wry amusement and frank interest. 'You poor little poppet. If he doesn't eat you the copier will!'

'What do you mean?' cried Abby indignantly. 'I'm nearly nineteen and I've no intention of being swallowed whole by anything or anybody.'

'Whoa! The kitten has claws!' he put up a defensive hand and pretended to back away. 'I didn't mean it! I only——'

'And don't call me kitten, please. I'm Miss Abigail Lynwood.'

'Delighted. But you are a kitten, soft, appealing, and cuddlesome. Will you scratch if I pick you up?'

His grin was irresistible, and Abby had great difficulty in keeping her face straight as she answered, 'Yes. Now, you were looking for Carola . . . Is it important? Can I——?'

'Important! I'll say it is. Look . . .' he fished a small glass phial carefully out of his pocket. 'This is the breakthrough!'

'Breakthrough?' Abby tried not to look blank. 'What is it?'

'Hush—it's top secret! His Highness isn't back, is he?'

'No—not till tomorrow morning.' Curiosity and the dawning sensation of beginning to belong to the new scene made Abby edge closer to the newcomer.

Grinning at her and making sleight-of-hand movements reminiscent of a somewhat ham conjuror, he drew the stopper out of the phial and passed it under her nose. 'Well?' he said at last, impatiently.

Abby was uncertain of what was expected of her. 'It smells like scent,' she said.

'Like scent, she says!' He closed his eyes and

assumed an expression of great suffering. 'Don't you know that this may make or break Balclairs new cosmetic and perfumery development? That——'

'But what is it?' she broke in. 'I hardly got the scent of it.'

'Number—' he peered at the label on the phial '—57 of this particular series—we're calling it Heinz down in the lab. But the exciting thing about this blend is that it seems immune to acid skin. Haven't you ever bought a scent that smelled gorgeous when you tried it at the counter, only to find that it either lost its perfume on you almost straight away or changed?'

'Yes,' she was longing to investigate this new discovery, 'only a week ago I bought some and found it didn't last, yet it's terrific on Emma, sort of wafts when she passes.'

'Because your skin chemistry affects a particular ingredient in it. But some of our girls in the lab have been testing the new possibles, and like this one best. Our man from Grasse thinks this is the one. Come on, try it.'

Nothing loath, Abby held out one wrist. He shook his head, and lightly touched her chin. 'Turn your head, kitten.'

He touched the dropper behind her ears, then to the pulse spots at her temples, and finally to her throat. 'Now wait a minute or so. Just walk round the office.'

Abby obeyed, and gradually the most delicious and subtle scent began to drift to her nostrils, intriguing because it would vanish for a moment and then return. Not floral, nor ferny, not the heavy muskiness of the East, but with a new, exclusive note about it that belonged strictly to the rarefied atmosphere of the French perfumery salons.

'Now come back to me,' he ordered.

Abby obeyed, and he drew a deep, questing sniff. An expression of bliss flitted across his good-looking face.

'*Ravissant!* Superb!' he breathed ecstatically. 'Let me have more!' Abruptly he caught her by the shoulders, drawing her close to him and taking further deep sniffs of the scent lingering beneath Abby's small, well-shaped ears.

'Tip up your chin, my sweet—ah, sublime! Kitten,' he whispered, 'do you realise you'll never be safe from a male while wearing this creation? You'll so inflame their senses they'll want to devour you—after they've loved you to death, of course.'

Abby was giggling helplessly, and also beginning to try to disentangle herself before the new potent creation intoxicated this bold young man to the extent of his own predictions. 'No!' she exclaimed, 'I'll take your word for it and——'

He dropped a kiss on her parted mouth, stifling the protest, and the door opened behind him. Across his shoulders, Abby's eyes widened with shock and dismay, and then disbelieving horror.

'Dickie! What the devil's going on?'

The newcomer strode into the office, very tall, very immaculate, heart-stoppingly handsome—and utterly daunting. Abby took a step back, and dimly the name he had spoken clicked into place. Dickie . . . Balclairs' big bad wolf . . . while . . . *Oh, no!* Abby groaned under her breath. Why did everything happen to *her*?

'Nothing, sir!' Dickie exclaimed. 'I just came over to see Carola and try a little experiment.'

'So I noticed,' said the great K.B. with a hint of acid in his tone.

'We didn't expect you back tonight.'

'Again, a trifle obvious.' K.B. tossed his briefcase on

to a chair, for the moment ignoring Abby, who had backed to the window. 'Well, what's the excitement about?'

'We've got it at last, K.B.' Dickie said triumphantly. He waved the glass phial. 'See for yourself! Or rather . . . smell for yourself.' He caught Abby's hand and pulled her forward. 'Come on, kitten! You and 57! Who could resist? This is going to be the——'

Abby never heard what it was going to be. Tugged forward by the impetuous Dickie so that the full revealing light of the window fell on her face, she stared with horror up into the grim expression of her future employer, and saw the same dawn of startled recognition in his eyes; aghast, disapproving, and ominous.

Her arrogant, scornful, one-time rescuer and the chief of Balclairs were one and the same man! The last man she would have chosen to work for: the last man ever to want herself as his secretary.

What had she ever done to fate to deserve this?

CHAPTER THREE

From a long way off she heard Dickie exclaim: 'Well, sir? What do you think?'

'My thoughts are unutterable at the moment—and the office reeks.' K.B. swung round, removing his shrivelling stare from Abby's pale face as though the sight of her offended him. 'We'll have a top priority meeting tomorrow morning.'

'Yes.' Dickie looked crestfallen. 'What time, sir?'

'Check my appointments.' K.B. flung the order over his shoulder at Abby as he strode from the room.

She looked blank, still stunned, and then made her way unsteadily to the desk. She opened the appointment book and turned the pages with trembling fingers. The following day held the information in Carola's neat, clear handwriting. She looked up. 'He has a meeting at ten-thirty, and a luncheon appointment at twelve-thirty. You'd better come over at nine-thirty—I don't know if he always comes in early,' she added uncertainly.

'He does.' With a wry gesture Dickie ran his hands through his unruly sand-coloured hair. 'Sorry about that. But who would have thought he'd have turned up at that precise minute—in quite his worst mood.'

Abby shook her head, knowing it wasn't really his fault—most firms accepted the presence of at least one skylarker among the staff—but unable to start explanations as to the true cause of the Chief's ill-humour. *That* she could never tell to a soul; she would resign first! Although she might well be out on her neck long before she had that drastic chance of salvaging her pride.

Dickie looked at her miserable expression and put his arm around her. 'Don't take it to heart, kitten. We caught him on the wrong foot—he's not usually quite so brutal.'

'Isn't he?' muttered Abby, with a certain inflection that Dickie wouldn't quite fathom. She drew away, remembering Dickie's reputation and determined not to encourage his somewhat overly sympathetic attentions.

'You'll have to learn to be like Carola,' he urged. 'She lets it all slide over her—water off the duck's back and all that—we all do.' His mouth compressed. 'But I was afraid the moment I saw you . . .'

'Don't worry, I can look after myself.' She closed the appointment book. 'Now perhaps you'd better go, in case . . .'

Dickie grimaced. 'Point taken—but I'll be seeing you again, my sweet kitten. So long.' Suddenly he stopped by the door. 'A word of advice . . . you'd better notify the others about that meeting tomorrow. First,' he began to tick them off on his fingers, 'M. Roseau, Bert Simmon, Lew Parker, and Jim Norris. May save you another black mood! Byee!'

Gratefully, Abby was hastily scribbling down the names. She found the numbers and hastily began the calls, hoping to catch them all before they left. Only with the last was she unsuccessful. Mr Norris's secretary took the message, and also the opportunity of a droll little welcome to Abby. She sounded fun, and Abby felt heartened, only to be jolted back to the alert by the buzz of the intercom on her desk.

She flipped the switch and heard the clipped sum-

mons in the voice she now recognised all too well.
Aware of the knot tying itself tightly under her midriff,
she grabbed pencil and pad and directed her feet across
the rich blue carpet to the door of the inner sanctum.
She tapped on the smooth polished panel, waited a
moment, then opened the door slowly.

'Come in, Miss Lynwood. We are not going to
devour you—yet!'

He was leaning back, arms folded, surveying her
with cool, sardonic grey eyes from the far side of a vast
desk. It seemed a mile away. He gestured briefly towards a chair by the desk end, his disturbing stare not
flickering as she started to trek through that mile of
ankle-deep grey carpet that seemed bent on impeding
her progress. All that was needed was a spotlight, she
thought bitterly as she reached the chair at last.

'Well, Miss Escort Girl.' A slight compression
tugged down one corner of his mouth. 'Don't we pay
our City workers a living wage?'

'Yes—no. It wasn't like that at all! I don't——'

'The system beat you? Or didn't prove as profitable
as you hoped?'

Abby stiffened, longing to lash out at that cynical
mouth. 'I'm a secretary, Mr Balclair,' she said with
emphasis.

'I trust that you are.'

She ignored the sarcasm and strove to remain cool.
'May I have your appointment book, please?'

'Help yourself.' He did not move.

Inwardly fuming, she scanned the broad expanse of
desk top, spotted the green tooled leather book that
was the twin of the one in the other room, and was
forced to get to her feet in order to reach it. *Of course
he couldn't shove it over into her reach*, she thought
furiously. Acutely conscious of being watched, she

opened the book and entered the note for the following morning, then added the names of the executives Dickie had told her to summon. She left the book open and pushed it back to him, her mouth compressed.

He glanced at it carelessly, nodded, then looked up at her. 'Well, what do you think of it?'

'What do I think of what?'

His brows went up. 'The initiation.'

She stared at him, instantly suspecting a trap and determined not to be caught.

'Come here,' he said impatiently.

Slowly she rose and moved warily towards him. Suddenly his hand shot out and closed round her wrist. Abby almost fell over and her heart bounded with shock.

'Ah!' He stood up. 'That should have set the adrenalin going. Do stand still, girl. Remember the warning!'

Abby trembled. She scarcely came up to his shoulder, and she prepared to fight to the last gasp for her honour. She had completely forgotten the perfume. All she was aware of was a sudden drift of decidedly male fragrance compounded of after-shave and sheer man. The smooth, silvery grey stuff of his suit and the pale green silkiness of his shirt exuded rather than hid the magnetism of its wearer, and the fingers imprisoning her wrist were right over the throbbing pulse. Abby's head swam. She pulled back, her wide eyes affronted.

'Mr Balclair!'

'No!' Abruptly he released her, and sat back on the edge of the desk. 'I'm afraid it does not inflame my senses, or urge me to devour you. Still less to love you to death. Actually, I hadn't heard that necrophily was in fashion now. But I'm not quite so susceptible as our chief technician.' He looked down into Abby's bewildered face and the sardonic quirk returned to his mouth. 'Also, I'm forgetting that you're scarcely in need of artificial aids to seduction.'

Abby gasped. She flung her notebook down on the desk and exclaimed: 'Mr Balclair! I am not an escort girl. And if I'm going to work for you satisfactorily you must let me explain and——'

He raised one hand. 'No explanations are necessary, Miss Lynwood. What you do in your spare time is no concern of ours. Nor, for that matter, are your morals. As long as your private life does not affect your working efficiency here.'

She saw that his expression had become chill and impersonal. He turned away and reseated himself behind the desk. 'I trust Carola has given you a briefing regarding our set-up here—which I assure you differs little from that of countless other offices. Judging by the expression you're wearing at the moment, you fear the worst. You need not. I do not expect the impossible from my staff, but I do demand the best of which they're capable. By that I mean you are not expected to be able to read my mind and grasp every detail of current projects during your first day here—but by the end of the month I may prove a little more demanding.'

He paused, and a glint came into his eyes. 'There's one other point. No doubt someone will inform you sooner or later that Dickie Tennant considers it his duty and his privilege to seduce every new and nubile female employee. I must warn you that her reign lasts only until the next personable girl arrives. But then I'm sure you'll already have recognised his particular line of strategy.'

'Then why are you bothering to warn me?' Abby strove to keep her temper from exceeding simmering point. 'You've just admitted that my private life and my morals are no concern of yours. Which they are not! How dare you talk to me like that?' she added furiously, flinging prudence to the winds. What if he did sack her? She'd be able to tell him exactly what she thought of him!

'I consider I have every right.' He surveyed her coolly, apparently unmoved by her defiance. 'After all, I did once extricate you from a rather unpleasant situation—one from which you appeared quite incapable of extricating yourself. So, no matter how much you may resent this, it's a trifle foolish to try to pretend that this incident never happened.'

'You needn't remind me. I remember it all too well.'

The bitterness in her voice made him tilt his head slightly to one side. 'Changing your mind about this job? Want to go back to the typing pool?' he taunted.

'Perhaps *you* would like me to change my mind. You've made it pretty obvious how much you despise me and dislike me,' she cried.

'Now you're being childish.'

'No, I'm speaking my mind,' she flashed.

His brows flickered. 'The honest type?'

'Mr Balclair. I simply want to be a good secretary. I'd prefer to be judged by my capabilities as such, and that only.'

'Good. Which brings me back to the question I didn't answer.' His eyes hardened. 'I warned you about Dickie Tennant because I consider a good chief technician and a loyal, efficient secretary of equal indispensability. I don't mind admitting that I'm going to miss Carola. I'm also aware of a great deal more that goes on here than some of my employees seem to credit. I know all about the little blonde analyst who came here as a cool, dedicated career girl.

Unfortunately she was just ripe for our Dickie, and she just couldn't take it when the new redhead arrived on switchboard. So a snivelling, lovelorn secretary will be of no use to me.'

Abby's chin went up furiously. 'Mightn't it be better to wait and see before you judge? You may see the first girl with enough sense to recognise the office wolf for what he is and act accordingly. For believe me,' she added recklessly, 'I have no intention of being seduced until *I* say so!'

'Famous last words,' he jeered. 'However, I'm a great believer in prevention when it's cheaper than cure. Have I made myself clear, Miss Lynwood?'

'Unmistakeably,' she said between tight lips.

'Good. We might as well clear the air right at the start.' He raised one immaculately cuffed wrist. 'You'd better get away now. It's after five.'

'I'm not a clock-watcher, Mr Balclair.'

'I wasn't aware of making that accusation.'

She met his gaze stubbornly. 'Is there anything else, Mr Balclair?'

'No, thank you. Goodnight, Miss Lynwood.'

'Goodnight, Mr Balclair,' she returned in equally frigid tones.

Abby went home that night in a mood that pitchforked her between the abyss of self-pity and the fiery peak of self-righteous rage. She hadn't yet quite recovered from the shock of discovering the identity of her new boss, and the prospect before her filled her with trepidation. Why did it have to happen to her? Just when she thought the benign fates were sending the job she'd dreamed of, with a super salary rise, plus the possibility of travelling abroad when he required his secretary. It was too much to bear. Also, there was the long-term angle. In some firms it was a case of once a secretary always a secretary, if you were a woman, despite the equal opportunities lark. But at Balclairs you could climb. In six months she could be P.A. to the Chief, and could even make the transition to the executive side. After that it depended on how ambitious she was and how hard she was prepared to fight in the rat race to power. It all depended on herself and her capabilities. Yes, Mr Drew had painted a very rosy picture of the opportunities at Balclairs. And now it was all washed out.

Abby glowered out of the train window. Why couldn't her big chance have come with a total stranger? A man who knew nothing of her apart from her references, and with whom her working relationship could be totally impersonal. Instead of with a man who had first seen her in a decidedly tawdry light.

Suddenly Abby shivered. The thought of the days stretching ahead were bad enough; the thought of being at his mercy was petrifying. She would always be conscious of that ghastly night with the lecherous Jack Keighley reaching for her with drunken paws and taking it for granted that she was at any man's call for the money. And Kelvyn Balclair had assumed exactly the same thing. Yet he had come to her rescue.

For the first time it occurred to Abby to contemplate his motive for doing so. Why, when he so obviously thought the worst of her, had he bothered? And why had he proved so contemptuous and hostile afterwards? But what if he hadn't bothered? said a small voice somewhere behind the resentment in her heart. Well, she would probably have made a run from the importunate Mr Keighley. There might have been a scene, and she might have blown it for poor Emma, but Emma herself would probably have dealt with the situation in no uncertain way.

But it hadn't worked out that way, and K.B. certainly hadn't forgotten. In his very first words to her today he had raked it all up again. Accusing her of being immoral. Well, almost, she amended. Saying her morals were no concern of his. It was practically the same thing, wasn't it? How dare he talk to her like that?

She exchanged a train seat for one on the bus, with another inanimate ten minutes to rail against the fates. The only thing to do was wish the coming month away as quickly as possible. For she couldn't possibly stay there now. She'd better tell him tomorrow she didn't want the job and he could start looking for another secretary, one who measured up to his autocratic yardstick of perfection—one with a hide more befitting a rhinoceros!

When Abby reached the flat she felt exhausted, and she groaned when she remembered that it was Monday, beastly Monday, and the flat chores all awaited her attention. The other girls were all out, and the larder was practically empty. Abby felt too tired to go down to the take-away, and without compunction she finished the one small slice of cooked ham left from the weekend. They were obviously all being wined and dined somewhere tonight, so they could make do with one-bag tea and biscuits.

Because of her additional travelling distance now Abby had to rise nearly an hour earlier in the morning. Suzanne stirred sleepily and complained of a headache, then begged Abby to bring her a cup of tea and an aspirin before she went out.

'How did it go yesterday?' Suzanne asked, one dark-circled eye half open.

'Terrible!'

'You'd better put on some lipstick, then.' Suzanne groped for the cup. 'You look like I feel!'

Make herself all glam for the benefit of his high and mightiness? Or ready for the attentions of Dickie Tennant—whose fooling around was to blame for much of yesterday's renewal of warfare? Not likely, thought Abby bitterly. Anyway, she was going to hand in her notice today, wasn't she?

But somehow Abby didn't quite get round to it that day. To start with there never seemed time. K.B. strode in at five to nine, bestowed equally charming smiles and good-mornings on Carola and Abby and remarked that he was thankful he had two secretaries that day because there was a mountain to get through. The two girls scurried through what seemed a mountain of letters in the first half-hour, then Carola sent Abby to sit in on the meeting, saying she might as well get used to it now as later. It was Abby's first experience of high-powered management, and unwillingly she admitted admiration at the sight of K.B. in action. He never missed a point, he demanded figures, facts and data, and Abby felt sympathy for the Technical Director of the new division who had not yet absorbed the full details of a market research survey commissioned by Balclairs. The fact that it had only landed on the poor man's desk that morning was no excuse, according to K.B.

Costs, quality control, package design and international marketing echoed round the big room, and ideas were thrashed out and sometimes discarded; the launch of the new perfumery and cosmetic division promised to be everything but unexciting.

That morning proved the prelude to a very busy two weeks. At the end of it Abby was still uncertain of what to make of her new boss. Since that initial

scourging of the first afternoon K.B. made no further
remarks of a personal nature. He appeared to have
adopted the attitude for which she had hoped, that of a
cool, impersonal yet courteous employer-to-employee
relationship. After Carola departed on the Friday,
bearing the silver rose bowl presented to her by the
staff and a wedding cheque for fifty pounds which was
the personal gift of K.B. himself, Abby felt the
renewed onset of butterflies now that she would be on
her own.

She was still frankly a bit scared of him, even though
most of her initial resentment was beginning to vanish.
She had to admit that he was fair, and during the following weeks she appreciated the fact that he gave her
advance notice when he required her to work late, and
remembered to give her an early afternoon to make
up for it. With confidence growing she learned
quickly and soon grasped his letter style, and her
instinct developed for when she could interrupt him
and when—no matter who it might be—she dared
not.

When the last day of the month came he surprised
her by saying he was pleased with her and her appointment was now permanent. She thanked him,
aware of an odd sensation that could only be anti-
climax, and emerged to find Dickie Tennant waiting
in the outer office.

'Well?' he demanded. 'Sealed the relationship or
handed his nibs the chopper?'

She told him, knowing the invitation to celebrate
would be forthcoming, and knowing she would refuse
it, as she had refused all his previous invitations to
date. It wasn't that she was unduly influenced by the
warnings she'd received but simply that Dickie did not
attract her in the least. Ten minutes of Dickie's kitten

serenade was enough, and the knowledge that she would spend the evening fending off his advances if she was weak enough to commit herself to a date with him was sufficient to keep her resolve firm.

'But why not?' He pulled an outraged face. 'It's not true what they say about me, you know. Look at me,' he wheedled, trying to manoeuvre her into a corner. 'Do I look like a breaker of hearts?'

'Yes,' she said simply, with an adroit counter-manoeuvre.

'It's a super disco,' he persisted. 'They're a terrific crowd, and afterwards——'

'I know. Your place—because mine's too far away. Sorry, Dickie,' she picked up her bag, 'no can. Now if I don't rush I'll miss the five-twenty.'

'Would you like a lift up to town, Miss Lynwood?'

Abby whirled at the different voice. K.B. stood at the open doorway, an enigmatic expression on his face as he looked from Dickie to herself.

Surprise made her stammer, and K.B. broke in smoothly: 'There's something I want to talk to you about . . . I'll be free in five minutes.'

He vanished back into his office, leaving Abby still staring. Dickie gave a snort of disgust. 'So it's like that, is it? I'd never have thought it of you! Not after——'

'There's nothing like that about it at all.' Abby put her bag down again, trying to conceal from Dickie the agitation that made her fingers want to twist at the bag strap. What did K.B. want to talk to her about? Was something wrong? Had he changed his mind about her? Suddenly Abby knew that this was the last thing she wanted.

'Isn't there?' Dickie looked furious. 'You watch it, my girl. He's got just as much of the old Nick as far as the girls are concerned as I'm supposed to have—only he doesn't usually try it on with his secretaries.'

'And he's not going to make an exception of me,' she returned, suddenly remembering. 'Don't be silly, Dickie. It'll be business, that's all.'

'Expect me to believe that! But then how can I compete with *that*?' he jerked an aggrieved thumb towards the inner door. 'Oh, well, kitten, don't say I didn't warn you.'

Abby was thankful to see him saunter out. Alone, she could try to pin down a valid reason why K.B. wanted to talk to her. She'd been in there all afternoon—less than ten minutes ago he'd told her the job was hers for keeps. What had he suddenly thought of during those minutes?

The office was so quiet now that Abby was struck by the frightful notion that he had played a joke on her. She dismissed the idea as quickly as it came; K.B. was definitely not in the pointless jokes class. Nevertheless she went to the outer door and looked out into the wide hall of the suite. Across its quietly opulent white and blue was the door which led into the comfortably furnished reception room. To her left was the door leading into the main outer corridor of the block, and to the right was the door of K.B.'s office. Not a sound. Surely he hadn't gone . . .

'Looking for someone?'

Abby jumped. K.B. stood behind her, having come through the communicating door into her room without her hearing a sound.

'No—I——' she stopped, knowing she couldn't very well voice her inane doubt.

'Sorry if I seem to have kept you waiting.' He gave her a curious glance, and she wondered fleetingly if perhaps he had thought she was about to sneak away.

'If you're ready . . .' He held the door back, and

hurriedly she darted for her bag.

It was an odd sensation, walking the deserted corridors and crossing the big reception hall at the side of the tall, dominant figure of Kelvyn Balclair. His long, lithe strides seemed unhurried, but it took two of Abby's steps to every one. Most of the staff had gone and only Big Fred, the doorman, smart as an R.S.M. in his grey uniform and war decorations on his broad chest, still paced the blue and white tiled expanse of the entrance hall. He touched his cap to K.B. and gave a whimsical but knowing little nod to Abby.

She hoped her cheeks were not pink as she approached the rakish, gleaming blue Aston Martin Vantage that was parked in the reserved space immediately outside. K.B., his features inscrutable, opened the passenger door and handed her in before going round to the driver's side. The powerful engine responded to a touch, and Abby sank back into the rich-smelling luxury of a prestige dream car.

The road slid away under them, and K.B. remained silent, increasing Abby's suspense. She played around in her mind with conversation openers, none of which seemed inspired gems guaranteed to break this daunting yet rather sweet ice. At last she swallowed dryly. If she was going to be sacked she might as well be sacked in luxury!

'Is—is anything wrong, Mr Balclair?' she asked in a constrained voice.

'I don't think so. Why should there be?'

There was a subtle inflection in his tone, and Abby, after an inward sigh at this unhelpful response, turned a discreet glance towards him. The strong, well-defined profile was quite relaxed, the hands on the wheel unflurried in their control, and his attention apparently concentrated solely on the business of driving. But as her gaze lingered a moment longer on that uncommunicative profile the dark brow flickered upwards.

Hastily she averted her gaze and with another small inward sigh settled back and summoned patience. Doubtless he would give forth when he was ready; meanwhile, this was more comfortable than the train!

'Thank you,' he murmured.

'What for?' She frowned a little.

'For sparing me a stream of small talk. I loathe being talked at while driving.'

'Oh—I'd better remember that in future.' *If there's going to be any future*, she amended silently, and suppressed a fatalistic grin.

The car sped on, purring sweetly, slowed and grumbled in a traffic snarl-up, then cleared through with a triumphant snort and leapt ahead. Presently K.B. slowed. 'Have you any special arrangements made for this evening?'

'No,' she said, after a moment of surprise.

'Good. We'll stop for something to eat. It's a bit early for a formal meal, but I know an eaterie round here where they'll rustle up something decent for us.'

Without elaborating further he drove on a little way and then took a turning off the main road. Instantly the awareness of traffic pressure eased and a couple of miles along the narrow country road brought them into a small village. There were a couple of farms, a huddle of new bungalows, then the square-towered church and the old high street with its couple of shops and the timbered pub set back behind the green. K.B. slowed and eased the car across the ford awash with a few inches of water, then headed up a narrow lane at the far side. Set back behind a wooded garden was a long, low rambling house with charming old latticed windows and a storybook well complete with old wooden bucket.

'The Lattices,' K.B. explained, driving into the big clearing that was invisible from the road. 'Newest and most popular eating place in this area. Friend of mine owns it.'

He led the way to a side door, and Abby had a glimpse of an oak-dark interior with tables agleam with glassware and cutlery. K.B. pushed the door open and stepped into the stone-flagged lobby. 'Anyone at home?' he called.

'Good God, old chap—you're a stranger!' A burly, middle-aged man in gold-rimmed glasses and green tweeds with patches at the elbows emerged from the inner door. 'How's the grind?'

'Still grinding,' K.B. said dryly. He drew Abby forward. 'This is Monty Allister. Monty—Miss Lynwood, my secretary.'

Introductions exchanged, Monty asked, 'What can I do for you?'

'A quiet corner to talk and something to sustain my secretary while I spring the shock of her life on her.'

'Ho ho! Like that, is it?' Monty chuckled. 'What would you like?'

Abby scarcely heard him. She forgot the delicious smell that was curling out from somewhere nearby, making her taste buds yearn. *What shock?* What did he——? Firm fingers slid under her arm, their pressure light but firm and insistent. She forced a smile at Monty. 'Oh, anything—something convenient that won't send your chef into hysterics and take his mind off the menu he's busy with,' she said wildly.

'What an understanding woman!' Monty exclaimed with a grin. 'Aren't you lucky, Kell? But then you always were a lucky devil. Well, how about a steak?

With French fries. Then you can have first pick of the sweets trolley.'

'That sounds delicious.' Abby was acutely aware of K.B.'s hand tucking its firm warmth under her arm again, guiding her along a narrow passage hung with horse brasses and old racing prints. A looped-back curtain at the end revealed the long restaurant, each table with its own small ruby-shaded wrought-iron lamp.

Monty stood aside. 'You know your way,' he said to K.B., and then winked at Abby. 'I'll send in the violins later.'

'My friend has a perverted sense of humour.' K.B. remarked dryly as he piloted Abby to the deep inglenook recess at the far end of the room. 'What would you like to drink?'

She slid into the high, panelled settle and looked up at him. 'If I'm due for a shock, Mr Balclair, it had better be something strong.'

'Name it.'

Abby sought for a suitable aperitif and her mind went blank. K.B. waited, not helping her out, while his mouth quivered at the corners. 'Campari,' she said hastily.

'Think it'll be strong enough?'

'It'll have to be, won't it?'

'I'll make it double strength!' He made his way leisurely back towards the entrance, and Abby was left alone in the silent room. She seized the chance to take out her compact and quickly check her appearance. That she would be dining with K.B. was the last thing she had expected when he made his sudden invitation before she left the office. She had retouched her lipstick and smoothed down her silky honey-brown hair, and on impulse pressed the switch of the table lamp before he returned, carrying the two drinks.

'Soft lights won't help, you know,' he remarked, setting down the glasses and then sliding into the other half of the settle.

'They'll go with the violins your friend is sending in,' she said recklessly. 'Do you always help yourself to the drinks?'

'If the staff are not yet in—yes.'

'What it is to be privileged!'

'It does oil life's wheels,' he returned coolly. He slewed round until his shoulders squared across the corner angle of the settle's high back and he was almost facing her. He gestured towards her with his glass, and she returned the gesture silently, wondering to what she was committing herself with the toast. His movement had brought his knee against her thigh, but the width of the settle scarcely permitted much in the way of evasive action. Abby edged her knee as far distant as possible from that disturbing pressure and studied the warm red depths of her Campari. It did not need much deduction to realise that he wanted something of her, and that something was of importance. But what?

If it concerned her work surely he would have dealt with the matter during working hours. It couldn't be personal; their respective lives and ambiances were as far apart as the poles, and he had never made any secret of the fact that he had a very poor opinion of her personal character. So why was he suddenly turning on this sardonic charm?

As though he were well aware of her trend of speculation, he asked: 'Have you a passport?'

'Yes.'

'Good.'

So they were going on a business trip. Paris? Bonn? She relaxed, only to tense again; he could have asked about her passport any time during the past month. So what . . .?

'You *are* prepared to travel anywhere?'

'Yes. I was told that was a condition of the job,' she responded warily. 'May I ask where—and when?'

'The Caribbean. Two weeks' time.'

The laconic answer took her breath away. Without thinking she exclaimed, "It doesn't sound like work!"

'I assure you it is.' His tone was dry. 'It's one of the most vital trips in Balclair's history. But doubtless we shall be mixing it with a little pleasure.'

The approach of a young waiter halted further disclosures. Their steaks would not be long and would they like starters? Abby chose melon and K.B. selected a prawn cocktail. Then he went on: 'You know that we're trying to get a foot in the American market, and we're angling after a small, now rather rocky, old-established pharmaceutical firm based on a small town in Louisiana. They've had a steady mail order business for fifty years, but they've lost ground steadily during the past few years, chiefly because the old man has refused to realise how much the cosmetic climate has changed. Vastly increased competition and high-pressure salesmanship combined with the fact that daughters are no longer content to go on buying old household names simply because Mother used them as a girl have eroded the shareholders' confidence so much the old man has had to get off his high horse. He's decided to retire and—having no son to carry on where he leaves off—sell out his fifty-one per cent controlling interest. This meeting in two weeks' time is to thrash out the terms.'

Abby was silent, her interest caught. She knew little of the machinations of big business, but she did know enough to realise that this could be a vital and risky step for Balclairs; the cost of getting it wrong in the U.S.A. could be calamitous. She returned her attention to the beautifully garnished steak that had been placed before her and waited for K.B. to continue.

'A banker friend of mine owns a villa in the Caymans—overlooking a beach supposed to be seven miles long on Grand Cayman—and he's put it at our disposal.' K.B. paused, glancing towards a party of about eight people, the first arrivals since themselves, who were taking their places with much laughter at a centre table that appeared to be decorated for a special occasion. 'Wonder what they're celebrating,' K.B. remarked, touching his mouth with his napkin and then topping up Abby's glass with Chambolle-Musigny.

Abby was not particularly interested in the new-comers, nor in what they might be celebrating. She said slowly, 'Thank you—Are you sure it's going to work out? I mean, isn't the American market over-loaded already?'

K.B. stopped eating and looked at her as though she had uttered heresy. 'Don't you know, my girl, that the last figures showed the retail sales heading for the two hundred million mark over there, and there's further growth potential yet to tap? There's got to be a slice for us, and I'm confident that our products can match any of the top names for quality, attractiveness and appeal.'

'Please,' said Abby hastily, 'don't let me spoil your steak! It's just that I wouldn't like to think the profit from the property deal got lost over the Atlantic.'

K.B. put down his knife and fork. 'Now you *are* spoiling my steak! Anyway, what do you know about our property deal?'

'Nothing, really.' She looked down at her plate—it

seemed safer! 'Just the usual grapevine rumours.'

'I thought as much.' K.B. prepared to eat again. 'I suppose you heard all about the millions we were supposed to make. Don't you know that everytime the tale's passed on it adds another nought?'

'I'm sorry.'

'And so you should. be.'

Monty rolled up at that moment, now resplendent in dinner jacket, to enquire if the steaks were up to standard. The two men chatted desultorily for a few minutes, then Monty moved away to cast a critical eye at the centre table and see that all was well at the send-off party, which, Monty had told them, was for a local man who was leaving the next day to take up an appointment in Saudi Arabia.

'He'd better make the most of his farewell drinks,' K.B. observed dryly.

The sweets trolley arrived, and its display of luscious looking confections was so mouthwatering Abby hardly knew which to choose.

'Have one for me as well,' suggested K.B. expansively.

Abby gave a horrified murmur. Finally she decided on a creamy concoction of feathery mousse and pale green meringue called Angelica Delight. K.B. waived the temptations of the desserts and saved his appetite for the Stilton. Coffee followed, and finally the seal of liqueurs.

The place was beginning to fill up now and the bonhomie of good eating was mellowing and warming the atmosphere. Abby was also beginning to feel very filled up. It was a long time since she had eaten such a superb meal. A delightful feeling of being at peace with the world stole over her and she sighed with uninhibited pleasure.

She shook her head bemusedly when K.B. asked if there were anything else she fancied. 'There's only one thing . . .'

'Yes?'

'What are we celebrating?'

There was a short silence, then K.B. sighed. 'Yes, I suppose we must get round to *that*.'

Abby turned her head and found he was looking at her, his grey eyes frankly surveying her small oval questioning face. She felt warmth stealing into her cheeks under the intensity of that cool grey gaze, and suddenly an incredulous suspicion flew into her mind. Surely he wasn't going to suggest . . .?

'Yes,' he broke in, smiling a little, 'I'm about to proposition you, Abigail, but not quite in the way you're thinking at this moment.'

Her eyes widened, as much at the unexpected sound of her baptismal name on his lips as at his uncanny foray into her thoughts. 'In what way, then?' she asked warily.

'I have a problem. A woman, needless to say.' He leaned back, and a certain hardness formed round his mouth. 'A very beautiful woman who's also very possessive, and who rarely fails to get what she wants. At the moment, the Atlantic is the barrier; in a couple of weeks' time it won't be. Do you follow me?'

'Not entirely.' Abby experienced a flicker of caution. She could not imagine K.B. unable to deal with any woman or any situation that displeased him.

'She's the granddaughter of Abelard J. Abelard.'

'The man you're going to meet to . . .'

'Exactly.'

'Oh dear!' Abby was beginning to get the picture. 'It could be rather awkward, couldn't it?'

'Very awkward,' he agreed. 'I've already ensured

that she's been told that I have a dreadful reputation, that I've several women in tow at present, and that I'll be bringing at least one of them on the trip with me. I'd have thought that to any girl of pride that would be sufficient. Would you agree?'

'Definitely.'

'I thought you might. But you do see that I need help?'

'Do you?' said Abby faintly.

'Isn't it obvious?' He leaned forward, propping his chin on one hand, and gave her an old-fashioned look. 'I need your help, Abigail.'

'Do you?' she repeated weakly.

'Yes. I want you to come on this trip with me, not just as my secretary. I want you to come as my woman.'

CHAPTER FOUR

So that was what he'd been softening her up for!

Abby's first reaction was more of amusement than shock. She'd known from the start she had to expect something, and when he began his rueful confidences regarding a somewhat predatory-sounding female she'd had a vague inkling that she might be called on to adopt the duties of a sentinel as well as those of a secretary. But this! After all that gorgeous food, well sauced with charm! He had a nerve!

'Now please . . .' He laid his hand lightly over hers before she could speak. 'Don't jump to the conclusion I think you've jumped to!. Hear me out.'

'I'm sorry.' She was steeling herself against weakening. She'd never imagined K.B. capable of such endearing tones. Honey on velvet! 'I couldn't. I——'

'Why not?'

'Because—because I just couldn't.' She knew she wasn't being very lucid, but something absurd was happening to her emotions. She felt she should be telling him indignantly what she thought of his suggestion, but righteous anger would not come, nor the initial tendency to giggle at the very idea of herself as K.B.'s 'woman'. Instead, she felt very sad, almost on the verge of tears. It was the wine; she was turning maudlin! 'It's impossible,' she said in a low voice, 'and you've no right to suggest such a thing.'

'What do you think I'm suggesting?'

'Does it need spelling out?'

'I think it does. Abby, it's purely a business arrangement.'

'It doesn't sound exactly like business to me!'

'It's not intended to sound—or look—exactly like business. That's the whole idea,' he said patiently. 'But as far as you're concerned that is all it is. Tell me, what's your objection to a few people who are total strangers believing for a few days that we're having an affair?'

'Because it isn't honest.'

'Honest?' He stared, then arid amusement hardened his tone. 'We're not considering honesty, my dear girl. This is expedience.'

He was beginning to sound more like his normal self and Abby felt sadder than ever. He said abruptly: 'I'll make it well worth your while, if that's what's worrying you.'

'It isn't!' she flashed.

'Then what is?'

She was silent, and an exasperated sigh escaped him. 'You're not under the impression that I'll expect you to sleep with me, are you?'

'Aren't you?' she said in a choked whisper.

He muttered an expletive, then controlled his tone. 'Listen, there are no strings attached. All I want you to do is hang round me and keep that damn female out of my hair. Just until we clinch the deal. Otherwise, how the devil am I going to keep giving her the brush-off all the time?'

'Is she so unattractive to you?'

'Frankly, yes.' His mouth compressed. 'I've no objection to equality or liberation for women, but I'm old-fashioned enough to want to be the hunter. The total reversal of the eternal man-woman business is out, as far as I'm concerned.' He sighed. 'Why the devil did Carola choose to get married at this precise time in history? She'd have done it like a shot and thought it all great fun. Oh, come on,' he said wearily, 'I'll take you home.'

Unhappily silent, Abby went with him to say good-night to Monty and make their way out to the car. It was dark now and a thin drizzle of rain was falling, depressing Abby's spirits even more. It became heavier as the car sped on, seeming to make an enclosure round the warm dark intimacy of the car interior, and the soft regular swish of the windscreen wipers began to have an almost hypnotic effect on Abby. *Why not . . .? Why not . . .? Why not . . .?* they seemed to reiterate in her brain. She was achingly aware of the silent man at the wheel, and of a wistful longing to be able to please him. Why couldn't she say what he wanted her to?

The wet and glistening landmarks were looming up now as he traversed the city and headed towards her home. Fleetingly she wondered at his remembering the way without asking her to remind him of the direction, and suddenly in memory she was back on that earlier journey. But now her wayward emotions remembered none of that previous acrimony; she could only recall his advent into her life that night and reflect that she still owed him a gesture of gratitude in return for his rescue, no matter how high-handed or censorious had been his manner.

She gave a deep sigh, thankful that the decision seemed to have been made for her, and sensed his head turn briefly to glance in her direction. But he said nothing, and moments later the car drew smoothly to a halt outside the house. The deep-throated power of the engine ceased, and the silence it left was suddenly compulsive. Looking straight ahead through the rain-spattered glass, she said quietly:

'I've thought it over. I—I'll do whatever I can to

help you—to make a success of the trip.'

He turned to face her, and the cold rays from the street lighting caught his features down one side, casting enigmatic shadows and making his expression difficult to read. 'Thank you, Abby. I felt sure I could rely on you not to fail me.'

His voice was cool, and she was aware of disappointment. But what had she expected? If not a return to formality . . . She said in equally cool tones, 'Thank you for the lovely meal, and for bringing me home.'

'It's a pleasure.' He inclined his head courteously, and again Abby experienced that twinge of disappointment. She swore under her breath. What did she expect—a goodnight kiss? The thought invoked a rush of warmth into her cheeks and hastily she murmured a goodnight and got out of the car.

But this was only a prelude to the logical sequence of thoughts that played through Abby's mind when she settled down to sleep that night. If she was supposed to be his girl-friend (she resolutely closed her mind to the assumption he obviously intended his man-eating inamorata to make) she supposed she'd have to learn to joke and chaff with him and not react if he occasionally put his arm round her, purely for appearances' sake, of course. But there would be several people there, and they'd be talking business all the time; that was the whole idea of the trip. Better not say anything to anyone, not even Emma, except that she was going there. The Caribbean . . . sun and silver sand . . . lagoons and moons and palm trees and carnivals . . . she'd never been that far away before . . . Golly! what was she going to *wear*?

This problem was resolved the following day, at least the most important part of the problem. After she'd dealt with the letters and made his coffee as though it were just another normal working day he bade her bring in her own cup of coffee and sit down.

'You're going to need clothes. Holiday gear.'

'Yes,' she hesitated, 'You won't mind if I wear informal gear, will you, sir?'

'Mind? I order you to. You'd better take a day off to get kitted up. You can either go to Harrods and charge the lot to my account or if you prefer to shop around the boutiques take a cash float and let me have the bills afterwards. Okay?'

Abby stiffened. 'I'll buy my own clothes, Mr Balclair. But I'd like some idea of what I'm likely to need—I don't want to get there and find I need something formal.'

He frowned. 'I wish you'd try to forget your allergy towards me and use your undoubted intelligence. You're going to do a job, and a working girl's salary will not run to the kind of wardrobe I expect to see you unpacking on Grand Cayman. You'll require at least two dresses for evening, beach wear, day separates, a glamorous house robe, the kind of lingerie you could be caught in, and at least six bikinis. In fact,' he paused and leaned back, giving her a very direct look, 'the sort of feminine garb my sidekick would be expected to possess.'

'Your sidekick?' Abby returned his gaze with widened eyes.

'You heard. I thought it was understood.'

Abby looked down, the rose deepening in her cheeks. She missed the cynical smile that curled the corners of his mouth.

'Come, Miss Lynwood,' he exclaimed, 'surely you're not worried about your reputation. Who's going to know? Except our prospective transatlantic cousins—and surely their opinions won't worry you. No one from this side will be with us, apart from old Mark, and he's the soul of discretion.' K.B. picked up his coffee cup and eyed her over the rim. 'I should have thought this little lark was just up your street.'

'And what exactly is that supposed to mean?' she said hotly.

He shrugged, then suddenly flashed her a charming smile. 'If we argue like this they *will* be convinced! Now,' he pushed his cup aside briskly, 'get Grahame on the line for me, please.'

The working days went on, while Abby tried to contain her doubts. If only he wouldn't make those hurtful innuendoes that made his real opinion of her so obvious. And yet he seemed so cold about the arrangement, making it quite plain that as far as he was concerned it was all to be merely a matter of expedience. Once, without stopping to reflect on what she was saying, she said; 'You could hire an actress to play the part— she'd do it more successfully than I will.'

'Getting cold feet, Abby?'

'In a way.'

'Don't worry. It'll be all right on the night, as they say.' Then his expression changed and became thoughtful as he studied her sober little face. 'I'll tell you why I won't adopt your suggestion. I don't want a stranger, no matter how convincingly she might play the role. I want somebody I can trust.'

Abby could think of no suitable reply to that. There could be no going back after that!

'By the way, he added, in that casual, throw-away-the-line manner that she now recognised as heralding something audacious, 'try and find something like this.' He pulled a magazine from a drawer and pushed it across the desk.

With a return of wariness she picked it up. It was

one of the Sunday colour supplements and it contained a fashion spread of swimwear. She knew without asking which one he meant. A sinuous, dusky model lay on some tropical beach with wavelets rippling over her smooth, lissome body. She was wearing the briefest of brief bikinis, and it was made of gold-thread lamé or similar material laced with scarlet thongs.

Abby studied it for a moment, trying to keep her face straight, then she put it back on the desk. 'Have you looked at the price?' she asked.

'Yes.'

'It's nearly forty pounds!' she cried in scandalised tones. 'And there can't be more than a quarter of a metre in the whole thing.'

'Ah,' he gave her a sidelong look, 'but it's a very special quarter metre, cut by a very special couturier.'

'Maybe, but I'm not paying forty pounds for a bikini! I'd want a lot more than that for my money.'

'It isn't your money.'

'*You* are not paying forty pounds for it, then.'

'The name of the stockist is at the back.' He pushed the magazine across to her again. 'Take it with you. And you'd better have tomorrow off to go shopping. Now don't argue, there's a good girl.' He passed one hand across his brow. 'I have a headache.'

'I'll get you some aspirins.'

Strange, he'd never complained of headaches before, Abby reflected suspiciously as she went into the luxuriously appointed bathroom attached to the office suite. In silence she returned with the aspirins and the glass of water, then retired to her own office to finish the letters.

It was with mixed feelings of doubt, guilt, and conscience that Abby obeyed orders and set off on her shopping expedition the following morning. But she would not have been human if feminine excitement and joy at being able to choose expensive garments did not override the dictates of conscience. If she did not follow his instructions she knew by now that he was quite capable of deciding to take charge himself. But she shopped wisely and as economically as she dared, selecting classic cut linen pants in cool lime green with a cotton shirt in toning checks, and more slacks in a thinner cotton in blue with a white shirt. To these she added gay flowered brief shorts with a matching tie-round skirt and coral halter top, and a white beach jacket, and at the last minute fell for a pair of scarlet pirate pants and a striped tie-front bra top. Then she recovered her strength with a cup of coffee and a tempting pastry, and started on the rest of the list.

By lunch time she'd completed her shopping as per command, with the exception of the gold lamé bikini. And here she baulked. It was a ridiculous price. And six was far too many. Three should be quite enough to ring the changes. She went back to the flat with arms aching under the weight of her parcels and stowed them all away at the back of her wardrobe. After making herself a snack lunch she had afterthoughts and dragged her suitcase out from beneath the bed. She tipped out the clutter reposing inside it and carefully packed all the new acquisitions, then locked the case. The thought of explaining away all those clothes was too daunting; it did not take much imagination to predict the comments of Emma and Dorice and Suzanne . . .

That afternoon she was surprised to find a stranger at her desk when she hurried in, much later than after her usual lunch break time. The little blonde with the perky, pointed chin and sharp blue eyes did not get up. She stared boldly at Abby.

'We didn't expect you back. Mr B. said you had the day off.'

'Mr Balclair to you,' Abby said tartly, divesting herself of her mac. 'You can get away now if you're filling in.'

'Oh,' the newcomer leaned back and swivelled gently back and forth, 'I'm Betsy Farlane—your new assistant. And you'd better watch it! I fancy your job.' She grinned insolently.

'Well, *you'd* better watch out—you know what happens to girls who start fancying things,' retorted Abby, instinctively repeating one of Emma's cheeky cracks. 'Have you——'

She didn't finish. The inner door had opened to reveal K.B. He surveyed Abby. 'Empty-handed?'

'I took everything back to the flat.'

He frowned. 'Did you get it?'

She knew what he meant and her mouth tightened. 'I did not!'

'Why not?' He gestured to her to come into his office. 'I suppose you couldn't find the shop.'

'I did find it,' said Abby indignantly, 'and you should have seen the girl there—her face was sprayed on and lacquered, not made up, and she looked at me as though I were something the cat brought in. I asked to see the model and she sort of looked down at me with her eyebrows going up the other way and said the biggest size they did it in was a twelve and I looked at least a fourteen.' Abby paused for breath and planted her hands akimbo on her slim waist. 'I am just a twelve. So I looked at it and pointed out a loose thread and asked her where I'd be when it gave way, then walked out of the shop.'

K.B.'s mobile mouth was struggling to retain its controlled lines. 'Then what?'

'I went to Marks and Sparks and got three there. They're super.' Suddenly she remembered the open door behind her and hastily shut it. She gestured. 'Is *she* going to be permanent?'

'It depends.'

'She'll take the place off you in five minutes.'

K.B. folded his arms and looked down at Abby, his eyes filled with glints of cool wickedness. 'You think I'd let her take it?'

Abby said nothing. She was beginning to cool down and realise that she had overstepped the calm, professional relationship she had intended always to maintain—even if it was far from easy with her unpredictable boss. But she held his challenging gaze and asked: 'May I venture my impression?'

'By all means,' he drawled.

'I don't think Miss Farlane will prove suitable for this office.'

He gave a slight smile. 'I'm assured that she's quite invaluable, extremely efficient, and has a gift for slipping in wherever she's needed.'

'I'm surprised someone hasn't snapped her up, then,' Abby observed.

'I've ceased to be surprised at anything.' He shot her a sidelong look. 'Someone will have to keep the place ticking over while we're away. Or had you forgotten?'

Abby hadn't, but she was realising how quickly the days were slipping away. In a week's time they'd be on their way . . . A mounting excitement began to possess her, and a secret, tingling agitation halfway between fear and anticipation that she couldn't quite explain. She'd be all right when she got there, she told herself firmly but without complete conviction. Certainly she couldn't back out now! Did she really want to? Even the veiled antagonism of Betsy failed to upset Abby during those last few days; she was kept far too busy, and she simply ignored the other girl apart from necessary office interchange. All the same, something would have to be done as soon as she got back . . . Her resolve stiffened on the final day before the departure.

K.B., so rushed and so impersonal now as to make it hard to believe that there was any pretend-personal relationship in the offing, said brusquely that morning: 'I nearly forgot . . . go down to the showroom when you've a moment and get them to fix you up with one of our special kits. See June if she's there, and while you're busy ask them to send up a new kit for me. We've got to be ambassadors for our wares!' he added.

Abby, who was basically independent and never took undue advantage of what is euphemistically known as perks, had not been in the showroom since the day Carola first showed her round, although she knew that most of the girls were always eager for samples, and Dickie never missed the chance of exerting a measure of conditional largesse. Today, it seemed she was to be treated as a V.I.P.

Urged on by the tall, elegantly dark June, intoxicated by the enchanting scents and attractive arrays of cosmetics, Abby revelled in a glorious half-hour of experimenting with lip colours, blushers, glossers and eye-shadows.

'You'll need a tinted moisturiser under our nature film,' advised June, 'and sun screener. And you'd better have some of our new sun soother pads in case you get burned.' She was deftly fitting the items into an attractive beauty case that looked more like onyx than the durable plastic of which it was made. Inside the lid was fitted a mirror, and on the outside was the distinctive monogram that was Balclairs' trademark.

Last of all June brought the perfume, two phials and a generous sized spray.

With a dramatic smile and gesture she handed Abby the case. 'Good luck—have a good trip. And don't work too hard!'

Abby returned to her office in jubilant mood with eyes aglow, to meet the curious stare of Betsy.

'Well, aren't you going to let me have a dekko?'

Wishing she didn't feel mean and guilty at her reluctance to show the other girl, Abby did so and watched Betsy examine the vanity case and its contents.

'Quite the little pet now, aren't you?' Betsy's smile was almost a sneer as she closed the lid. 'Well, make the most of it while it lasts.'

'What do you mean?'

Betsy shrugged. 'I've been with the firm for seven years and I've seen them come and go. You'll have your day. But don't make the mistake of falling for our Mr OKay B., or you'll regret it.'

Abby stared. 'I've no intention of doing so. Do I look so naïve?' she said furiously. 'I hadn't been here five minutes before I was warned about Dickie Tennant, and now . . .' Words failed her and she seized the beauty case, putting it beside her handbag on top of a filing cabinet.

'Dickie's only a sexpot,' said the other girl scornfully, 'but *he*,' with a thumbed gesture towards the inner door, 'has class. And he knows it. So don't get any big ideas just because he throws you a few samples.'

'I have no intention of getting any ideas about anybody,' Abby retorted, 'and I suggest you do the same. Now, if you're supposed to be working perhaps you'll get those copies of the Harwall report done and filed.'

'What do you think I did while you were enjoying yourself just now?' Betsy said smugly.

Abby fumed. She had no idea why Betsy had taken such a dislike to her, and why she should sound so spiteful. With an effort she maintained her temper, and got on with the last jobs that waited to be cleared before she departed. But the other girl's jibes had stung, and effectively dispelled all the pleasure that the little session with June had generated. She was thankful when the clock rolled round to five and Betsy took herself sulkily homeward. Abby tidied her desk, watered the office plants and hoped that they wouldn't be forgotten while she was away, then went to report to K.B. that all had been left in order.

'Good. Now why aren't you away, you conscientious child?'

He seemed in a very good humour, and Abby relaxed, despite being uncertain about the mode of address within his compliment. 'Is there anything else, Mr Balclair?' she asked in her routine manner.

'No—unless you can persuade the phone to ring.'

'Shall I try for you?'

'Not this one,' he shook his head, then made a dismissive gesture. 'See you tomorrow—we'll be in Miami by this time, give or take five hours!'

The phone rang as Abby began to say goodnight. K.B. snatched up the receiver, his expression changing and exclaimed: 'Julie . . . what happened——?'

Abby closed the door quietly and went from the office. Who was Julie, to cause that urgency in his voice? Sighing, she donned her outdoor things and gathered up her belongings. It was no business of hers whoever Julie might be . . .

Somehow the flat little reflection left a feeling of sadness . . .

Despite the excitement of the next twenty-four hours the name of Julie kept coming into her thoughts whenever there was a lull. When she looked at her neatly packed case that night and decided there couldn't possibly be anything she'd forgotten; when she was relaxing tiredly in the bath and when she was trying to will herself to get to sleep; during the journey to the airport next morning, and during the long hours of the flight itself.

K.B. was seated two places away from her, next to Mark Winstan, the financial director, and the two men were deeply intent on their low-voiced discussion, once lunch was over. Who was Julie? Certainly her name was not on the list of anniversaries in Abby's memoranda book. Not that there were very many names in it, Abby thought. His mother, who lived in the West Country and never came near Balclairs, a sister called Helen who was with her diplomat husband in Rome, and a youthful distant cousin aged nine, called Antonia Margaretta—a name which by the remotest stretch of imagination could not be shortened to or confused with Julie.

So Julie must be a girl-friend. Perhaps that very elegant and attractive girl who had been with him that night at the Hawaiian Lei . . .

Abby sighed. The two men had ceased their discussion and were reclining back, legs outstretched and eyes closed, obviously prepared to pass the boring hours of a transatlantic flight in sleep. The announcement began about the film; Abby decided she might as well watch it. Suddenly everything had become all very prosaic . . .

The flight passed without a hitch. Abby felt disappointment at seeing nothing of Miami except intense blue sky and a throng of Americans in holiday gear

amidst a great deal of airport noise before boarding the
Cayman Airways plane for the final short lap of the
journey. Here at least she was allotted a window seat
and so had her first glimpse of the blue Caribbean
sparkling below like a sea of sapphire crystal dotted
with green velvet studs of islands.

Mark said indulgently, 'First time, Abby?'

She said, 'Yes—it's beautiful!'

K.B. gave a slight smile that held a hint of uninterest.
'First time's always a novelty.'

Abby was silent. He couldn't have been more impersonal. Obviously the pretence was not due to start
yet!

But she could not repress her excitement once they
had landed and were in the car K.B. had ordered for
hire for the duration of their stay. The heat, the brilliance of green and the dazzling white of the modern
buildings in George Town—Abby had never seen so
many international banks together—and the vivid
glowing colours of flowering shrubs all combined to
generate a sense of discovery. And then they were
driving along the coastal road, following the Seven
Mile Beach, along which were strung the new hotels
with their landscaped gardens and holiday chalets.

The island was only about twenty-two miles at its
longest stretch, looped around North Sound, its big
natural harbour, and Abby hoped she would have a
chance to explore. She loved walking, rambling and
swimming, and had missed these pursuits since leaving
her native Northumbria.

Within a few minutes they reached their destination, a low white sprawling villa well away from
the road and screened by a dense shrubbery of tropical
plants and trees. The villa was built in the
Mediterranean style with whitewashed walls and red-

tiled roofs, set in charming informal gardens of lawns
and wandering pathways amid a riot of tropical greenery. Nearer the villa were series of tiled patios and
raised flower beds on different levels, and there was a
courtyard with nooks and crannies and quaint old urns
from which bright blossoms tumbled and trailed. Two
young children came racing out, all smiles, to meet the
newcomers, followed by a plump woman in a gaily
patterned dress who shooed the children away and introduced herself as Evalina, the Caymanian housekeeper. She welcomed them in the lilting accents which
Abby was to discover was one of the charms of the
local people and told them that the two youngsters
were her grandchildren.

'Wonderful how everyone smiles here,' observed
Mark as he helped K.B. unload the luggage. 'It's a
pleasant change from the couldn't-care-less service I've
come across in some places. Now, I wonder . . .' He
stopped and started to laugh. The children, who looked
about eight and ten, were disappearing into the house
staggering under the weight of two large cases almost
as big as themselves. K.B. dived after them, relieving
them of their self-inflicted burdens and tactfully offer-
ing a couple of lighter items to salvage juvenile pride.
They looked up at him, a certain provocative glint in
their eyes, and K.B. bent to hear some confidence,
maintaining a suitably sober countenance.

Watching him with the two children, Abby felt a
plaintive little tug at her heartstrings. Although he was
still in the formal, lightweight suit in which he had left
England there was already a subtle difference in his
mien. A glimpse of warmth and humour, and something very like tenderness that Abby certainly had
never glimpsed before. He straightened, his expression
grave.

'This is Sarah,' he glanced down at the diminutive girl in her crisp, pink-dotted dress, 'and this is Georgie, her brother. They've volunteered to act as guides if we want to see over the island. They've also informed me that they live in Hell!'

Abby blinked, and Mark's pleasant features creased in a humorously suspicious frown. Then Evalina chased the giggling pair into the villa. She laughed, round cheeks appling and black eyes sparkling. 'It's quite true. There is a place here of that very name, and they love to watch the visitors' faces when they tell them. Little devils! Now, sirs, would you like drinks or showers first? Or,' she looked at Abby, 'a cup of my special tea?'

'Anything, as long as it's a drink,' said Abby, who was very hot, very thirsty, and longing for a few quiet moments to unwind and escape the jet whine that still seemed to linger in her head.

'It's a very special tea—the first thing Mrs Brenton wants when she gets here, and she always has it sitting out there ...' Evalina pointed across the spacious airy living room to where the fourth side consisted entirely of sliding patio screens which opened to a heavenly vista of white beach and palms and sea. Beside a clump of feathery palms stood a thatched hut open on all sides in which could be seen loungers and a bamboo table. Evalina's pleasant features urged Abby to follow her mistress's tradition without any further delay.

'It sounds lovely,' exclaimed Abby, surreptitiously easing her thumbs into a waistband that seemed to have got tighter during the long flight.

'You don't want tea!' K.B.'s voice sounded at Abby's side, and she turned her head sharply, starting at the unexpected nearness of him. 'Tea is for plump matrons with tired feet. Look, I'm just going to see that all the baggage is in and sort out the rooms. Why don't you have a quick shower and slip into something cool? Then we'll have drinks.'

Those grey eyes considering her flushed face made Abby feel slightly unsteady. She tried to meet that long gaze with unconcern. 'I must go down to that beach—instantly! Besides, I think she's gone to make that tea . . .'

As nonchalantly as she could she strolled away from him, across the patio and along the coral and shell path to the beach. But immediately she felt the soft white sand under her shoes and stood by the edge of the water, watching the creamy ripples lapping invitingly like the lace froth of a shimmering swirl of jade-green silk, Abby wished she had followed K.B.'s suggestion and got into a bikini. The sea seemed to wait like a silken gown to enfold her. Smiling away the regret, she turned and saw Evalina coming from the villa, a tray in her hands.

A few moments later Abby was ensconced on a lounger under the thatch of palm, her shoes kicked off and her hair loosened so that the light breeze could steal with its coolness round the hot nape of her neck. The tea was iced, with lemon and something else which Abby couldn't recognise but which made the scented jasmine drink deliciously fragrant and refreshing.

The sun was going down now, creating a glory of scarlet and saffron and printing intricate black traceries through the shadowing palms and fern that wavered with each whisper of breeze. Languor stole over Abby's body and she closed her eyes. Idly she pondered on the whim of fortune that bestowed the luxury of a holiday home like this set in one of nature's jewelled playgrounds; but there was no envy in the fleeting thought, for the moment she was content to drowse . . .

The sun slipped lower. Dimly she heard the distant voices of the children, then silence came, broken only by the rustles of greenery and the cry of a bird over the sea. Little disjointed reveries took her wayward thoughts one way and another; there would be work to do, it wasn't a holiday. But it would be lovely to look up from her typewriter and see all this . . . and there'd be time for swimming and seeing the island . . . and it might be tremendous fun pretending to be K.B.'s girl-friend . . . Somehow she didn't feel so scared about it now she was actually here . . . would he put his arm round her? She supposed he might, to make the play-acting look genuine . . . she'd have to try not to giggle . . .

Abby's lips curved at the thought. She couldn't really imagine K.B. being romantic, not with herself . . . his lean, attractive features formed on the screen of her closed lids, his mouth firm and serious, and Abby gave a tiny sigh, letting imagination wonder about . . . *but imagination had never been so vivid!*

The mouth was quite real! Warm, light, lingering and sensuous. Abby's eyes opened wide enough to pop out, and saw grey eyes, black lashes, and the dark outline of his head. An incredulous tingle shot down her spine and she gasped against his lips.

He straightened, and stood looking down at her speechless expression. 'Coming for a swim?'

'You—you k-kissed me!'

'First rehearsal.' An intriguing quirk lifted one corner of the mouth that was still the cause of the disturbing tingles besetting Abby. 'There has to be a start soon, you know.'

'What do you mean—a start?' She stared up at him,

knowing very well what he meant but not yet prepared to have it all properly punctuated. Then she stopped staring, equally unprepared for the sight of this hitherto unseen K.B., tall and lithe and masculine in brief dark blue swim trunks, a white towel slung carelessly over one broad shoulder. Head down in case she was blushing coral, Abby began to scramble up, exclaiming, 'I can't swim until I unpack something to swim in.'

'Why bother?' A firm hand came out to assist her. 'It's a private section of beach. Shed the trappings of convention—and your inhibitions. Go back to nature,' he said airily. '*We* won't mind.'

Abby was outraged. 'Are—are y-you suggesting that I swim in the *nude*?' she stuttered.

'Well, the water will be warm enough, I should think,' he said with wicked innocence and his head on one side as though he were giving the matter earnest consideration.

'You can't be serious, Mr Balclair,' Abby said, smoothing her dress down primly. 'I think I'd better go and——'

'Just a moment . . .' his hand stayed firmly round her wrist as she turned to escape, 'we have to sort out one or two details, so we may as well get them straight now.'

The habit of obedience in the efficient secretary was too ingrained in Abby to allow her to refuse, even though her boss looked anything but businesslike, at least to Abby's idea of how her boss should look, at that moment. She waited, only to find herself being drawn forward until she was very close to her infuriatingly unpredictable boss.

He put both hands on her shoulders and regarded her with unfathomable eyes. 'To begin with,' he said, 'you've exactly twenty-four hours to get used to the idea of forgetting the Mr Balclair. And the sir.'

'Yes, but what do I call you?' She kept her gaze firmly at the level of his shoulder. 'I mean, I know you want me to pretend that we—that we're——'

'Having a full loving and caring committed relationship?'

'Oh no!' Abby's eyes widened upwards. 'You can't pretend a thing like that unless it's real. But even if I pretend to be your girl-friend I'm still your secretary. I mean, won't they think it rather strange? If you were really having an affair with me wouldn't you have got another secretary who might be expected to keep her mind on her work?'

For a long moment he stared at her, a considering light in his eyes. Then his mouth curved sardonically. 'Abby, you brilliant child! That aspect never occurred to me. Yes, I can't see Thea being convinced, or even greatly concerned if she thinks I'm merely having it off with my secretary. Abby, you're going to have to be extremely convincing.'

'You should have hired Emma. She'd have played the part to perfection.'

'Who's Emma?'

'My flat mate—you've seen her. That day with the children when——'

'Oh, yes,' his mouth twitched, 'the Aunties Anonymous. I remember. The winsome urchin type—sleek steel in suede boots. No, Abby. It had to be someone I can trust—not someone capable of making capital out of me afterwards.'

'What you should have had is a wife,' Abby stated flatly.

'Don't be naïve,' he chided in taunting tones. 'This is precisely the kind of trip businessmen do not tote their wives along on. Anyway, that would only add twice the spice as far as Thea is concerned.'

'From the sound of her, I'm going to be a total failure,' Abby said despondently and ungrammatically. She sank down again on the lounger and shook her head. 'I'm just not cut out to be a femme fatale.'

'But that is exactly what I had in mind.' K.B. settled himself at her side on the lounger. 'Because you're the complete opposite in nature to Thea it's going to throw her a bit—I hope.'

Abby sniffed. 'You mean she's going to wonder what you see in me.'

'I never said that—or even thought it. Don't underrate yourself, Abby. Remember that the shop with the showiest goods in the window isn't necessarily the most interesting inside.' He paused, and a trace of the old scornful impatience came into his expression. 'For heaven's sake! There's no need to go on with the naïve innocence act. You must have picked up some idea of what the business is all about during your sorties into the escort game. Why can't you turn on the charm for me?'

She could not answer. The harshness in his voice hurt too much and renewed the cold despair with the knowledge that despite his lighthearted charm of a few moments ago he had not changed his first, disastrous impression of her character. She opened her mouth, wanting desperately to try to explain, then pride kept her silent. What was the use? She tried before and he had simply shut her up, refusing to listen.

'I remember, you know,' he said abruptly. 'The way you hung on that drunken oaf's words, grinning at his jokes—I bet they weren't fit for any girl's ears—and letting him paw you all over the dance floor. That rose dress . . . did you bring it?'

The sharp demand startled her. 'No—it wasn't mine. It's Emma's. And I hated him! Please believe me.' Her wide eyes pleaded for understanding. 'I hated every minute of it. That's why I was so thankful when you——'

'All right, Abby, there's no point in raking it all up again,' he interrupted brusquely. 'But just tell me; surely I don't raise the same revulsion, do I?'

'Oh no!' Horror at the very thought drove out everything else. She looked up into his grim face, almost frantically. 'That's why I agreed to try this—to sort of repay you for——'

'Then start trying to co-operate.' He gave a jerked sigh of exasperation. 'Try to remember not to call me sir when Thea's around. My friends call me Kell, if that's any help to you. All you have to do is take your cue from me and try to play it with some pretence of response. And try not to gasp like a startled innocent when I do this . . .'

With the speed of light his arm went round her waist, his other hand trapped her chin, and the hard pressure of his mouth stifled the very reaction he had so accurately predicted.

It was a thorough, very proficient kiss, made forceful by more than a hint of suppressed anger and accompanied by the kind of embrace that left Abby in no doubt about the expertise of K.B.'s lovemaking talents.

The effect on Abby was beyond her power of analysis. When he released her she felt winded, as though a hurricane had raged round inside her unprepared body and was not yet inclined to relinquish its turmoil.

He picked up the towel that had slipped to the ground and stood up, glancing at the fire of the setting sun. In the rich light he looked like a stranger, tall, broad-shouldered, with a strength of torso unhinted at when clothed in the formal garb of business. His dark hair was ruffled, lifting slightly in the wayward breeze, but the arrogance of superb self-possession was still in every line of him and Abby released a slow, long-pent-up sigh.

He turned his head briefly, as though he heard the soft betrayal of emotion, and smiled with a trace of mockery. 'Don't look so worried,' he said dryly, 'you'll improve with practice.'

Practice! The word reverberated in her brain while she tried and failed to think of a suitable riposte.

He made a movement away, with the obvious intention of loping down to the saffron-flecked sea, then he checked his stride and glanced back at her. 'By the way, there's a box on your bed—you're getting careless, Abby, the way you leave things behind.'

He strode away then, leaving Abby staring after him like one bewitched. What was he talking about? She hadn't left anything behind. She'd remembered the portable typewriter, plenty of stationery, everything she could find about the deal they were hoping to clinch. She'd better go and find out!

She stood up and walked on legs that felt decidedly weak into the villa, where Evalina showed her to her room. Yes, there was a large flat shiny gilt box lying on the bed. And it certainly didn't look like the kind of box that contained office equipment!

A moment later Abby was delving with feverish hands into the sea of tissue paper within. Scarlet and gold emerged, the lamé bikini, and with it something she had not seen before; a vivid scarlet beach jacket, fingertip length with a high mandarin collar. It completed a stunning ensemble.

At last she went to the mirror and slowly held the

jacket against herself. Its colour instantly picked out the fire K.B. had lit in her cheeks a few minutes previously, and the darkened eyes that looked back at her from the mirror held something like trepidation in their depths. Once more he had shown her how futile it was to disobey his commands.

Abby suddenly became aware that she was trembling. She was also just a little bit afraid. But never had she known that being afraid could be so exhilarating . . .

CHAPTER FIVE

THEY dined by candlelight that first evening, beneath a rich canopy of tropical stars whose brilliance more than vied with that of the golden, flickering candle flames. A warm soft breeze played on Abby's bare arms, and the sea sighed across the darkness, as though its whispers would convince her that it was indeed true; she was actually here in this island paradise: it wasn't just a dream. Nor was the unexpected gift. Nor was that little rehearsal!

Her cheeks began to burn. The memory was unexpectedly pleasurable, much more so than the feeling of guilt with which her conscience instantly reacted. She'd be very foolish if she started silly day-dreamy reminiscences about *that*. Had she forgotten what K.B. was like when he wasn't being charming? And that this was all part of the job?

With this stern injunction to herself Abby took her elbow off the table and her silly dreamy chin out of her hand and sat up very straight, assuming the kind of expression she wore when preparing for a particularly trying day in the office.

The two men seemed temporarily to have forgotten her existence as they discussed various points concerning the meeting which lay ahead. K.B. picked up his glass of wine and looked reflectively in its pale golden depths. 'Yes, I think we have to play these next few days very patiently.'

Mark nodded. 'You're right. Abelard has no intention of parting until he's ready—despite the pressures of his family. He's playing the field like a Victorian deb in her first season.'

Kell smiled faintly. 'Except that Abelard has forgotten and survived more seasons than I care to contemplate. So I feel we should go easy, no matter how impatient we feel. He and his party are our guests first and business competitors last. Don't forget that his colleagues will be anxious to add to the pressures—it could just disarm him to find a relaxed atmosphere instead of boardroom tactics.'

Abby felt some surprise. Already her mind had become attuned to the cut and thrust of business deals where timewasting or the slightest sign of weakness could be fatal to the desired outcome. She looked at Kell. 'But it could be bought and sold twice in two weeks. Aren't you afraid of some other company putting in a higher bid?'

'There is that risk. But I happen to know that Abelard has issued a public denial of all rumours concerning the possible sale of Delicare Enterprises, which gets him off the hook for a little while.'

'If he can muzzle Thea!'

The look Kell turned on Mark was not amused. The older man grinned and shook his head. 'Just make sure the price isn't too high, Kell,' he said meaningly.

'I've contingency plans in hand to meet *that* danger,' Kell said grimly, and for a moment his glance flickered towards Abby. 'But like most contingencies the prospect of their success is somewhat uncertain.'

His words kept returning to Abby later that evening when she retired to the large, beautifully furnished and airy bedroom which had been allotted to her. There had been something in his tone that jarred her, as though he expected her to fail him and was already regretting as foolishness his notion to bring her along on the trip.

She slipped free of her filmy undergarments and shouldered into the new, glamorous negligee of drifting white chiffon, not bothering to fasten it and merely drawing its edges carelessly across her as she went towards the adjoining bathroom. There was something strangely disappointing, almost hurtful, in the thought that Kell might be resigned to her failing him. Even though it was true that she'd hated the idea of letting a crowd of strangers believe she was having an affair with her boss—a particularly intimate affair, she told herself firmly—and the man in question had given her ample evidence of just how tough, grim and intolerant he could be, she was discovering an odd little desire to break down that tough and intolerant barrier and reach the real man beyond. What was he like? With friends and family, when he relaxed and became human?

Abby's hand opened the bathroom door, her nostrils registered the scent of masculine toiletries, and her gaze took in the tall figure with spiky wet black hair in the act of donning a white terry robe. Simultaneously Abby gasped with horror, felt her cheeks go crimson and backed towards the door, stammering frantic apologies.

'I'm sorry—I didn't realise—*Oh!*' Her heel caught in the hem of the slightly overlong and full negligee. She struggled for balance, grabbed desperately for something to hang on to, and felt a handful of terry robe instead of the shower curtain that was nearest. The hard, muscular arm under the robe flexed but did not give.

Kell's other hand caught her shoulder, gripping firmly until she steadied. 'Don't apologise,' he said in bland tones, 'it may tend to get monotonous after a few days.'

'What?' Abby stared at him, spirit returning. 'Anyway, what are you doing here? I thought——'

'We're sharing a suite.' His tone was unchanged. 'Didn't you realise?' Ignoring her exclamation, he went on; 'I deemed it best. These rooms are on the short angle of this villa, at the extreme end. It was quite a problem to allot the accommodation suitably and please our guests, as well as making quite clear exactly what the set-up is.'

'Set-up?' Abby's lips parted as the full meaning of his words percolated. 'You mean I have to share a suite—a bathroom—with *you*, all the time we're here?'

'That's the general idea. I thought it was understood.' His hand still lingered on her shoulder. 'There is a certain impression it's essential to convey.'

There could be no doubt in his meaning, and outrage mapped its own impression on Abby's small oval face. 'Oh yes—I understand perfectly!' she cried. 'It's a wonder you don't expect me to do the job thoroughly and share your bed as well!'

His mouth flickered at one corner, then firmed again, and the line of his jaw was hard. 'If you meet me very often like this I may be tempted to consider that a very good idea. I must admit I hadn't realised quite how tantalising my new secretary would look—with her hair down.'

His gaze travelled over her appreciatively, a survey both deliberate and challenging, and suddenly Abby began to realise something of the picture she must present standing there, clutching filmy folds of gossamer and lace that revealed more than they concealed. Then the arrested line of his glance filled her with horror. She became aware of the swell of her breasts which must be all too visible to that interested scrutiny, and her hands flew up across those intimate features as she cried indignantly, 'You can't be serious! And you know I'd never have dreamed of barging in here if I'd known you——' she was backing towards the door and escape as she spoke. 'I'll make sure it never happens again, or——'

'How disappointing!' He was following her, to stand in the doorway and watch her embarrassed retreat. Amusement was open in his eyes now and the curve of his mouth devilish. 'You're blushing, Abby.'

'What do you expect?' Her expression demanded to know why he had the cheek to follow her into her bedroom. 'I think you might have warned me!'

'I forgot. But there's no need to look so worried. I'll forgive you,' he added magnanimously.

At a loss how to cope with this situation, Abby backed a bit farther and stared at the tall, rakish figure propped nonchalantly against the door frame. He seemed disinclined to move, and she closed her eyes with despair as she suddenly realised how promptly a recent wish was being granted. Only a few moments ago she'd experienced that strange little desire to surmount the barrier and discover what K.B. was like as a man. It seemed that if she made the slightest unguarded move she would be more than making that discovery!

'Come here, Abby,' he bade softly.

His arms were folded, light glistened on the dark hair still wet from the shower, and in his eyes was an expression that told Abby he was seeing her in a completely new way. Her heart was beginning to thump uncomfortably fast, and she gave an almost imperceptible shake of her head.

His eyes never wavered. 'Come on. You know you want to.'

'I don't!'

'You're a terribly poor liar, Abby.'

'I'm not!'

'Don't argue.' He moved lazily, stretching out one hand. Waiting to be obeyed.

It was like being hypnotised. Abby tried to stop her feet starting the hesitant small steps across the thick blue pile of luxury carpet that rendered those steps eerily soundless. She stopped just out of arm's length and stared defiantly up at him. 'Yes, sir?' she asked deliberately.

'I'm not fooled.' His mouth curled a little. 'You're not feeling obedient, are you?'

'Since you ask, sir—no.'

'I thought not. Why not be honest and admit you're curious?'

Her denial came far too quickly, and he smiled slightly again. 'You're still wondering if I'm human, aren't you, Abby?'

Scarlet rushed into her cheeks. She tried to stammer a shocked protest, but her tongue refused to form suitable words. He shook his head, a silencing gesture, and said dryly: 'I'm well aware of the doubts you've harboured in that respect where I'm concerned.' Without haste, he reached out one hand and caught hold of a thick tress of her soft lustrous hair. He tugged at it, not roughly, but firmly enough to force Abby close, close enough to feel the material of his robe touch her, see the dark hairs on the bare chest in the vee of white lapels, and sense the whole masculine strength of the man held for the moment in check there.

Abby was so tense her body felt as though it would snap if she tried to move. Her toes dug into the carpet and gripped the soft thickness of it, and her heart throbbed like a dynamo. There was a bar of navy piping along the lapel of his robe, and two silk-embroidered initials interwoven into a monogram on the breast pocket just level with her eyes. The outline of those initials began to dance and dazzle on her vision, as though they were imprinting themselves permanently on her brain, and a sensation of warmth, trembling and sensuous, was coursing through her body.

He moved, and the firm mouth came down very close to her face. Abby's nerves twanged, her breath caught in her throat, and she saw the glint of white teeth.

'You know something, Abby?' he said silkily. 'By the end of this trip you may have found out.'

Abruptly he released her and turned away, to cross to the far door and say casually over his shoulder: 'It's all yours. Goodnight.'

The sense of anti-climax was unbelievably weakening. She put one hand against the door to support herself until the dynamo inside her calmed down a bit, then she drew a deep quivering breath and prepared to commence the mundane business of teeth brushing and showering. But she made sure the little ornamental gilt fitting was secured on the far door before she unrobed and stepped under the cooling fountains of spray.

Her emotions were mixed and tumultuous, and the rushing shower, far from absorbing the heat from her body, seemed only to hype up her feverish senses until her nerves were taut to snapping point. When she reached for the thick fluffy robe and huddled into its enveloping folds her movements held an urgency that betrayed the need for concealment as much as the necessity to dry herself. Not for worlds would she admit to two certain emotions that threatened to dominate every other sense now the shattering little encounter had ended so abruptly.

She was experiencing anger and shock, she told herself desperately. What else? Certainly not disappointment. That was ridiculous. If Kell had kissed her she—she would have slapped his face. He had no right to expect her to share his bathroom! And there had been no need for play-acting then! Or rehearsals! Then all that cross-talk about his being human. All she was likely to discover were further examples of how inhuman he could be.

But Abby could not quite convince herself of all this. When she slipped between cool silken sheets and stared into the darkness all that scary, exciting emotion came back, filling her with a new, aching longing no man had ever evoked in her before.

Abby awakened late next morning after a restless night, feeling distinctly at odds with the world.

It was the heat and the change of climate, of course, she assured herself firmly. It would take a day or two to get used to it. But that was no excuse for sleeping in on the very first morning, no matter what had happened last—*no!* she whispered vehemently under her breath, forbidding her mind to clock up yet another re-run of that little scene in the bathroom. No wonder she had tossed and turned restlessly for most of the night with her imagination working overtime. And now she had to show a cool face in public, where the cause of it all would be as arrogant and self-possessed as ever.

At least she didn't appear to be last in to breakfast. There was no sign of K.B., which, after a disappointed lurch, her heart decided was just as well, but Mark was there, a cool-looking glass of fruit juice in one hand, when she walked out on to the patio where a big circular white table was set for three.

Mark looked avuncular and reassuringly amiable, his grey hair ruffling in the slight breeze and his pleasant, middle-aged features taking on a perceptive and sympathetic expression as he greeted her.

'Do I detect a touch of good old jet-lag?' he grinned.

'What's good about it?' Abby asked wryly, taking the chair opposite.

Mark shrugged. 'Well, it's as good an excuse as any for bags under the eyes—mine!' he added hastily.

'I'm glad to hear you qualify that statement, Mark.'

With the dry tones a shadow crossed the patio, and Abby looked up, straight into the sardonic gaze of K.B. He had obviously been for a swim, and droplets of spray still glistened on his broad shoulders and chest. Standing there, in brief blue swim briefs, a towel hung over one shoulder and his dark hair spiked with moisture, he looked more like a handsome young jet-setting playboy than a hardworking, ruthless man of industry.

'Sleep well, Abby?' he asked.

'Moderately,' she responded after a pause, painfully conscious of his pervasive glance and the warmth beginning to burn in her cheeks.

Fortunately Evalina chose that moment to appear and by time the conferring over what to have for breakfast was done Abby had regained her self-possession. It wasn't just a case of getting acclimatised to new surroundings; she seemed to have reached the stage where she had to get acclimatised to K.B.'s presence at each time of meeting, she reflected wryly.

The guests were not arriving until the following morning and Kell and Mark discussed their plans for the day.

'A crash course on the island, I think,' said Kell, 'to familiarise ourselves with the layout.'

'To give us the advantage of appearing to be on home

ground, naturally,' Mark grinned.

'Naturally,' returned Kell, straightfaced—'How well you read me!'

'Long practice.' Mark turned the grin towards Abby. 'You know something? I've a feeling it's going to be a far more exhausting day than a working one back home.'

Mark's surmise proved not far from truth. It was a very long day, and Abby could scarcely conceal her exhaustion when they got back to the villa late that evening after a comprehensive tour of the island. There had been no time allowed for the pleasure and leisure of discovery, of joyous appreciation of the endless vista of crystal blue sea, lush green and glowing splashes of blossom colours in this Caribbean paradise as Kell moved relentlessly on, familiarising himself with layout, routes, entertainment and sporting facilities and eating places and mentally mapping out provisional itineraries for the entertaining of his very important guests.

Certainly there wasn't a trace of the threat embodied in his taunting remarks of the previous night. He had reverted to the K.B. they knew so well, a ruthless man in determined pursuit of a particular objective. Anything but human, Abby reflected tiredly as she sipped her nightcap while Kell discussed with Mark a fishing trip he'd arranged for later in the week. Abby hoped she wouldn't be expected to accompany the party. She'd seen films depicting the playing and landing of the big fish and experienced the same sense of revulsion evoked by bullfighting. Abby could see no sport in a long, goading, pitiless struggle that ended in death for the loser. What was it that made man want to hunt and shoot and kill just for the fun of it? she wondered sadly. Was it some ancient genetic heritage that periodically cracked the veneer of civilisation, sometimes even to let the bloodlust run so fiercely that man forgot sport and turned on his fellow men, and innocent women and children . . .

'—and try to look a little happier!'

'I—I beg your pardon!' Abby started, and saw Kell looming above her, his expression as sardonic and impatient as his voice. What had he been saying to her?

'I said try to remember to play your part as though you meant it.'

'Oh, you mean . . .'

'Yes, I *mean*,' he said grimly. 'I'm relying on you to counteract one complication.'

'Oh, have a heart, Kell! Can't you see the kid's dead tired?' Beyond Kell's tall figure Mark was looking equally irritable and impatient, but in a different way. Mark went on: 'I know that if I were about to attempt the job you're expecting of Abby your present attitude would be guaranteed to make me take the next plane back—after telling you exactly what you could do with your lousy job!'

In the silence that followed Abby's gasp was quite audible. She waited for the explosion that must surely result and hardly dared look up at Kell's face. When she did another shock coursed through her. Something like grim amusement was tugging at the corners of his mouth. He glanced down at her.

'No need to look so astounded! There's at least one man in the world who's allowed to tell me exactly what he thinks of me. Which he does quite often. It seems you have a champion,' he added dryly. 'But don't try to take advantage of that interesting fact too often.'

Abby did not reply. She could only realise with dismay that Mark must know about Kell's plan and her own role in that plan. Suddenly she remembered Mark's look of sympathy that morning at breakfast, and with sudden shock she wondered if he had unwittingly overheard any of that scene the previous night. Even as common sense told her that Mark's room was at the other side of the villa and he couldn't possibly have overheard herself and Kell, she saw Kell give a small gesture that betrayed his own tension and tiredness.

'Mark's right. We're all bushed.' He gave Abby a somewhat meaningful look. 'I'll give you half an hour's start for the bathroom.'

Mark also had caught and interpreted the meaning look. 'So if Abby can't complete her evening ablutions in thirty minutes that's just too bad.'

A flush of fury rose in Abby's cheeks. Forgetting any sense of business discipline, she glared at the two men. 'It's worse than being married!' she cried, and stormed from the room.

Her impetus carried her halfway across the broad, centre hall around which the spacious villa was built before her steps slowed on the beige and blue pattern of floor tiles, and she realised it might have been sensible to stop and look for the light switch. She went on more slowly, avoiding the long white wrought iron plant holder, and Kell caught up with her at the door leading into their suite. His hands imprisoned her shoulders.

'And what do you know about marriage?'

'Enough to know that the stardust wears off very quickly,' she hissed, trying to push his hands away.

He resisted her efforts quite easily. 'Such cynicism! So you don't believe in marriage?'

'I never said anything of the sort!' She twisted round till she could look at his face, but the shadows hid his eyes. 'Will there be anything else, *sir*?' she asked coldly.

The movement, and her question, had been a bad tactical error. It made it so easy for him to slide his hands round her waist and pull her hard against him. 'Yes,' he said calmly, 'I want to kiss my secretary goodnight.'

Abby felt caught in a trap of her own making, a trap that was rapidly disturbing her senses. She strained away. 'The game doesn't start until tomorrow!' she exclaimed desperately.

'So what?' He gathered her closer. 'It's almost midnight now.'

The dark shape of his head was outlined above her, then dipped down as her eyes instinctively closed. His hard mouth moved against her lips, exploring a little, unhurried, then with increasing force crushing their softness. His hands caressed her back, stroking with gentle insistence that beguiled Abby into stillness under his touch. Her heart began the familiar agitation that was predictable now whenever Kell approached, let alone touched her, and the warning hammers of defence started their clamour in her brain.

'Kell . . .' she tried to say, and draw back before everything got hopelessly beyond her control, but the word came out only as a small stifled moan and her body didn't seem to have any strength left to resist that sudden extra tightening of arms that seemed to have sensed the fluttering impulse to escape.

Under the persistence of his mouth and the sensuous pressure of hard masculine contours moulding the softness of her body Abby was lost. A molten flow of delirious madness flooded her limbs. Her hands found their own way round his back, fingertips exploring the warm, tantalising feel of his skin under his thin silk shirt, and her mouth parted at last, tremulously seeking, receiving, giving . . .

She felt him sigh against her, felt her mouth bereft as he left it, to trail a smouldering fuse of kisses along her cheek and down her throat. She touched his lean jaw with unconsciously urgent fingertips, wanting his mouth again, and for a moment he looked down at her, his shadowed features unfathomable, as though he would deny her mute longing. Then with scarcely restrained force he took her mouth.

The small, fierce consummation went through her like an electric shock. Far, far away a tiny voice of reason tried to penetrate the force of desire and warn that she might regret this wild foolishness. But she did not want to hear. She wanted only to go on experiencing this new ecstasy and its promise . . .

His kiss was no longer controlled, fiercely demanding, and his caresses more urgent. His hands found their way beneath the soft flimsy folds of her voile blouse and explored the satin-smooth warmth of her back. His touch on her bare skin made every nerve contract, and for a moment in time her heartbeat stopped. Her body waited, captive to every sensation he was awakening in it, while the flimsy lace scrap of her bra gave way to determined fingers, and a thrill like a tongue of fire shot through her as his caressing hand homed to her breast.

Abby moaned softly under the teasing, erotic play of his touch. Never before had a man taken her breast, peaking the nipple, curving her body harder against the male shape of his own, arousing a new throbbing ache deep in the most secret recess of her body.

Kell stopped his kiss for a moment. 'You're a passionate little thing under that stubborn exterior, aren't you?' he whispered, his voice husky and slightly unsteady. 'So why do we have to fight first?' He let his mouth slide against hers and his touch feather where it would.

Abby opened eyes already drugged by his love-making. 'I don't—you do,' she murmured somewhat incoherently. 'I——'

His kiss silenced her again, then he whispered, 'So what are we going to——'

His sentence was never completed. Light flooded the hall, a sharp oath escaped Kell, and there was another dismayed exclamation.

'I'm sorry! I didn't know you were still——'

Abby, instantly freed, saw past Kell to where Mark stood in the doorway of the room she and Kell had left only minutes previously. The older man looked embarrassed, almost shocked, and Abby felt fiery colour burn all over her. She tried frantically to straighten her dishevelled clothing and turned blindly to escape. But Kell's arm barred her way and fell about her shoulders. He had regained composure almost instantly and said easily:

'Of course you didn't. Not to worry. You'll get used to it!' His arm slid from Abby's shoulders and during its descent delivered a decidedly familiar slap across her small rear. 'You've only twenty minutes left, my sweet. Or doesn't it worry you now?'

The meaning in this last question was so blatant that her cheeks crimsoned afresh. She looked up at Kell and could not believe what she saw; mocking glints in his eyes and a quirk to match at one corner of his mouth. He was *laughing*! He was actually laughing at her after the way he had . . .

In that moment Abby plummeted back to sanity. His unconcealed amusement set the touch-taper to embarrassment, shame at the way she had lost control, and anger.

'Yes!' she snapped. 'It worries me. But something else worries me even more. Just what is Mark going to get used to? What's he going to get used to seeing?'

The glints were instantly extinguished. 'Oh, for God's sake, Abby, stop being such a baby. A few kisses! Do you have to take everything so deadly seriously?'

'A few kisses!'

'What else?' His tone was clipped, and challenging.

She stared at him, unable to credit the change a few moments could wreak. It came to her, with a rush of sadness, that a change had also come into their relationship. It was there in the way he looked at her, in his whole attitude. Suddenly she knew that he wanted her, that he would have been quite prepared, given any encouragement, to take that little episode a good deal farther, in fact, to its logical conclusion. But now he was as angry as she.

Trying to calm her own emotions, she said unsteadily. 'The girl whose benefit all this is for isn't even here yet. I fail to see why you——'

'Tried to break down the barriers?' he interrupted. He gave an impatient gesture and his eyes had gone hard. 'If I'd realised . . .'

He left the words unfinished, and Abby's hands clenched. 'Yes, Kell? If you'd realised what?'

'Oh, forget it!' he snapped. 'But don't try me too hard with the outraged dignity—I'm losing patience and——'

'You're losing patience!' Abby forgot her attempt to cool the situation. She could only read all the implications in his angry attack, implications that made her feel cheap and foolish. Her mouth trembled, then hardened, and her fists balled again. 'I think you'd better make up your mind exactly what you want to carry out your stupid plan. A baby—or a girl who's deadly serious about everything! Or do you want someone you can make fun of just as the fit takes you? But then you never did have much of an opinion of me, did you? You——'

She gasped as he took a menacing step towards her. Putting one hand out defensively, she cried, 'Why don't you admit it? I happened to be convenient at the time you needed someone, and I was foolish enough to feel I owed you something. But I'm not going to be used like this! I'll try to do what I promised, but no more. And when we get back you'd better find yourself another secretary.'

She paused a second to gulp a breath. 'One who's more accommodating—and who doesn't mind being made a fool of!'

She turned blindly away and stumbled into her room, slamming the door behind her. Tears were stinging her eyes and a great aching lump was compressing her throat. *I hate him! I hate him!* she whispered fiercely under her breath. *He's cruel and arrogant and uncaring, and I wish I'd never set eyes on him!*

In the silent, still unfamiliar room, her hands responded to the conditioning of a lifetime, pulling off her clothes, folding them roughly and putting them in a small heap on a stool ready for laundering, thrusting pins carelessly into her hair to keep it away from her face while she creamed away make-up, then shook out the folds of a clean nightdress. No shower, no bath tonight, even though she felt hot, tired and sticky. Not for worlds was she going to risk another encounter tonight with K.B.

She switched off her light and stretched out tense and quivering between the cool sheets, biting her lip to keep at bay the need to weep. What kind of a fool was she to cry over him? A bigger fool than the one he'd made of her. And the way he had made love to her, the way she had let him . . .

Abby stared miserably into the darkness, trying to force calm into her disturbed body and agitated mind. But without success. She was too stubborn and too uncertain of herself to admit the truth: how dangerously near she was to falling in love with a man who had in turn despised, castigated and mocked her. And she was too inexperienced to recognise the true cause of the turmoil that raged within her. Innocent until this moment of the torment of sexual desire aroused and left unfulfilled, she could only seek desperately for comfort in pride, trying to reassure herself that she hadn't been a total fool. She'd made it quite clear to K.B. that she had no intention of being treated like a cheap chattel! She——

A groan choked in her throat as full realisation dawned of just what she'd done. Yes, she'd given her notice. She'd announced that she was leaving. She'd told him to find another secretary!

After two weeks' time she'd never see him again . . .

CHAPTER SIX

THE view from Abby's window looked incredibly beautiful at dawn next morning, but it failed to lift the leaden weight of misery that bowed her spirit. She heard Mark's voice outside, not far away, and then the crisper deeper tones that made her tense and stand utterly still until they ebbed into the distance. The two men must have gone for a swim, she thought dully as she prepared to face whatever the new day was going to bring. Not that anything could be worse than last night.

If Abby expected K.B. to betray any sign of disturbance, concerned or otherwise, over her precipitate announcement she was doomed to disappointment that day. He was more suavely cool than ever, making no reference to Abby's taut, unhappy expression or the air of strain she was unable to conceal.

Shortly after ten he departed for the airport, in good time for the arrival of the guests whose private plane was expected to touch down at eleven, and fresh tension began to grip Abby. For the first time she became conscious of curiosity about the girl she would soon be meeting, the girl who seemed to inspire so much dread in K.B.

Abby shook her head musingly as she pondered her choice of garb for the all-important meeting. She still found it impossible to believe that K.B. was actually scared of a possessive female who was determined to get her hooks into him. K.B. was more than capable of dealing with any unfortunate girl who dared to believe

she might call the tune. Abby put the lime linen pants
back on the rail and took down the coral cotton,
frowned, and irritably jabbed the hanger and its light
burden back in place. He was dealing with the matter,
wasn't he? And using herself in the process. Because it
suited him to maintain a relationship with this pre-
sumptuous female while simultaneously placing himself well out of reach, until he had successfully achieved
his objective.

But wasn't there a flaw in the psychology of his reasoning?

Abby reached the end of the wardrobe rail and stared
somewhat absently at the splash of vivid scarlet and
the glints of gold—extremely small glints of gold.
Didn't K.B. realise that his plan would almost certainly
misfire? Didn't he know anything about a woman's
reactions to the advent of a rival? Did he really expect
Thea simply to accept a new presence without a
murmur? Without temper, tantrums, spleen and sulks?
If he did he could be in for the shock of his life.

The thought supplied the faintest suggestion of balm
to a very bruised spirit and with a distinct sense of
schadenfreude Abby reached for the scarlet and gold.
Why not? She was going to be a red rag to a bull today.
That was what he wanted, wasn't it?

She was sitting on the patio, sipping from a tall,
frosted glass and trying to will herself to relax, when
the sound of a car drifted from the front driveway.
Her immediate impulse was to leap up and run towards
the sound, but she resisted it and stayed unmoving,
the chill from the glass transferring itself to her hand
and making a little echoing shiver reach her spine. She
heard voices, male at first, then the husky feminine
tones that seemed instantly to convey a challenge.

The voices stopped, and Abby realised the owners

girl who had been in Kell's party that awful night at the Hawaiian Lei. There was no mistaking that hair! Even though it had been dressed in a formal evening style and the angle at which she had been sitting that evening had presented mainly her profile to the envious, miserable Abby suffering at Jack Keighley's table.

A slight frown narrowed Thea's fine brows and Abby stifled a groan of dismay. She would die of shame if Thea recognised her. But for the moment Thea did not appear to be struck by recollection, and she turned away as the other two men and Mark came out of the shadows. Kell completed the introductions and Lee, the younger man, said, 'Hi,' with a friendly grin while Abelard, Thea's grandfather, nodded unsmilingly. But his handshake was warm and firm, and his blue eyes held a directness Abby liked. Suddenly she took to him, instinctively recognising a blunt honesty and a shrewd personality that would eschew duplicity.

It seemed her liking was reciprocated. When everyone had drinks and the social graces had been exchanged it was by Abby that Abelard chose to sit. He remarked dryly that their names 'sure matched,' and added that he had been looking forward to this break for weeks. She was a little surprised and then sympathetic when he volunteered the information that he had had a pacemaker fitted during a heart operation six months previously.

'This is why I have to let go. I can't give the company my best—and my wife says she wants to keep me a few more years yet.' He sighed, and Abby glimpsed something of the wrench it was proving for this man to surrender the power he had held for so long. 'But it's going to be hard to step aside,' he went on sadly. 'My father started the company sixty-three years ago, and he put me to work the day I was fourteen. We didn't go for degrees in those days. We did it the hard way. I fetched and carried in the laboratory and cleaned the place. Until the day I was actually allowed to fill some pots.' He smiled reminiscently. 'And we never used pots with thick bases!'

Abby gave a little laugh of surprise at the unexpected confidence. She was familiar with the sense of disgust when an expensive jar of cosmetic proved to consist of more artfully constructed container than contents. Oddly touched, she said, 'I'm very glad to hear you say that, Mr Abelard.'

'And I've never allowed the company to get profit-conscious to the extent of cutting on value for money. Even though Thea and my nephew say I'm old-fashioned,' he added with a distinctly old-fashioned look that made Abby smile again.

'There's nothing old-fashioned about giving value for money and playing fair by the customer,' she said promptly.

He nodded, seeming in a mood to reminisce. 'Ever notice when you buy shampoo it's in a bottle like a steam-roller took a shine to? Then it falls over if you touch it.' His tones were flat, wry and unhurried. 'We used to package our hair-care in cute little country pots with pictures of herbs on. Our older ladies used to collect sets of them. But these days they'd waste space on supermarket shelves.'

'Your packaging sounds lovely, like the kind of style coming back now, country-fresh, natural products,' Abby said thoughtfully.

'Too late for me. It's the old story of being in the right place at the right time.' He gave the amber liquid in his glass a reflective swirl before he drank abruptly. 'Tell me, Abby: is Britain still as conscious of tradition? Or is it lip service, and is plastic conformity taking over everywhere like it is in most places?'

'It's taken—if you're talking about progress,' she said dryly.

'No. I'm talking about economic growth, Western style.'

Abby looked down, uncertain of what he expected of her and a little uncertain of exactly what were Abelard's personal views on the state of the world's complex economic factors. More important, in view of a certain need for present diplomacy, how far he reconciled the overall picture with his own personal advantage. She said slowly, instinctively knowing what he wanted to hear, 'I know it's not always easy to keep the best of the old and adopt only the best of the new, and keep faith with one's conscience as well, but as far as tradition goes K.B. will certainly streamline and mechanise. One thing he won't do is use containers with thick bottoms!'

Abelard did not respond to her tentative smile. He was staring at her, almost as though he hadn't heard her words.

'Have we met some place before?'

'I—I don't think so!' Startled, she returned his probing gaze, then recollection brought sheer dismay. There had been no doubt about Thea's presence that ghastly night at the Hawaiian Lei, but somehow Abelard had not really registered on Abby's consciousness. He had been simply an anonymous grey-headed older man, sitting with his back towards the table Abby sat at with the objectionable Jack Keighley. And the older woman who had made the fourth member of K.B.'s party that evening had not left a clear memory. If she had seen them the following day Abby doubted if she would instantly have remembered where and when she had seen them; her whole attention had been taken by K.B. His attractive looks and dominant personality had certainly fired her imagination with silly little daydreams, she thought bitterly.

Forcing her attention back to the present, she shook her head and responded quite truthfully, 'No, we've never met, Mr Abelard.'

'Strange,' broke in a cool, husky voice, 'because I've got that impression too, and I've been trying to place her.'

Thea was standing there, slightly to one side of her grandfather's chair, a frown puckering her brow. Abby tensed under that searching assessment, then Thea shrugged carelessly, the movement sending ripples of golden fire through that glorious hair. 'It'll come back to me, don't worry.'

This assurance was calculated to do exactly the opposite, thought Abby, beginning to feel like a pinned butterfly with a permanent worry. She heard Thea ask her grandfather what he'd found so interesting in his talk with Kell's little assistant, which placed poor Abby firmly in her humble place, Mark came and took her glass, asking if she'd like another drink, and conversation became general. Gradually the threads of tension eased in Abby.

Abelard leaned back, closing his eyes against the sun. He looked very tired and pale under his tan. Thea finished her drink, then turned to Kell with deliberate challenge in her eyes.

'When are you going to introduce me to that heavenly sea?'

'Do you need an introduction?' he returned coolly.

'Not really.' Perfect white teeth glistened provocatively between parted red lips. 'It's just the way my temperature says it needs cooling.'

'You'd better say when.' His own mouth was enigmatic.

'Now?'

'Why not?'

Thea smiled with satisfaction. 'Give me two minutes to find my room and change.'

Kell glanced at Abby, and the message was quite clear. With a small inward sigh she got up and showed Thea to her room. Mark had already taken Thea's opulent white leather and gold-stamped luggage into the guestroom set aside for her, and there Abby left the titian seductress to her own devices.

It took surprisingly little longer than the promised two minutes to bring Thea back, displaying her undeniably superb body in the briefest of brief white bikinis. She had pinned her hair carelessly on top and she carried a white towelling jacket with the nonchalance of one who had no doubts at all of her own attraction.

She leaned against a low, decorative wall that edged part of the patio and upturned her face to the sun until Kell appeared a few moments later. She caught his hand carelessly as they moved together across the garden. Abby noticed that he made no attempt to free himself.

'Coming?' He glanced down at her with a casualness that hurt.

Before Abby could reply Thea laughed. 'In that? You must be joking, Kell. You don't let a creation like *that* get wet. Come on!'

Abby stared resentfully after their lithe, striding figures. In the space of a very short time Thea had made her feel garish and overdressed in a bikini of all things, and then proceeded to draw everyone's attention to the fact. The crystal blue sea shimmered into a myriad sparkles as tears stung her eyes and she brushed the back of her hand across the moisture, trying not to give in to the unfairness of it all. She glanced round.

Mark and Lee had gone indoors, and Abelard had donned dark glasses and was reclining in a lounger. It was impossible to tell whether he slept or surveyed the scene. Suddenly Abby got up and went into the house, where she changed into jeans and a yellow cotton shirt. K.B.'s idea—if it were that—of dressing her like a glamour girl had certainly misfired, she decided bitterly. And he ought to have accepted the fact that she wasn't the jet-set type, she was a working girl whose priorities had always been laid strictly in order by the hard vicissitudes of life. Things like gold lamé bikinis had been very low on the list. She looked at her scrubbed, make-upless face and tied-back hair above the clean crisp cotton and wished with all her heart that K.B. had left her out of his plans for this trip. For they were doomed to failure, and with her logical mind Abby could not fathom why he'd ever bothered about them in the first place. He'd just gone off hand in hand with Thea, hadn't he?

Disconsolate, she returned to the garden, to find Abelard alone and no sign of Kell and Thea.

'Where is everybody?'

She shook her head. 'I don't know. Would you like a drink?'

'No, thanks, honey.' Abelard stood up and stretched. His previous traces of weariness had vanished and in the stocky figure under the navy blue stretch towelling sports shirt and white pants there was a suggestion of coiled strength and latent power. Abby glimpsed another facet of a very strong personality. 'Let's explore, huh?'

Abby hesitated. The V.I.P. guest was getting restless already! Well, she'd better try to entertain him until someone with rather more authority returned to do so.

'Okay.' She smiled. 'Would you like to go along the beach?'

Abelard gave her wry look. 'Not really. I want to see the island.'

That he would simply appropriate the car and take off on an imprompu tour of the island had not occurred to her. But she had no doubt that here was another male who was used to getting his own way.

After they'd enjoyed a delicious lunch of seafood and a white wine like nectar imagination was allowed to run riot as they examined the fascinating collection of ancient coins and artifacts at Pedro's Castle. As Abelard escorted her back to the car Abby ventured to mention that perhaps K.B. and the others would be wondering where they'd got to.

'We're adults, and they're not kids that can't be left,' was the uncompomising response. Abelard closed the door when she had entered and suddenly grinned down at her. 'Wonder if Henry Morgan buried any treasure here?'

Abby gave up worrying and decided, as things seemed to be out of her hands, that she might as well enjoy herself. For some unexpected reason of alchemy she felt a strong rapport with Abelard and he appeared to like her company. In a very short time it was as though they'd been friends for years. They stared at the wreck of a freighter on the reef and speculated about the numerous ill-fated vessels that had met their doom on the treacherous coral down through the centuries. There was time to watch the deft-handed women of Gunn Bay at work making rope from palm, time to stand and make bets on how high would spout the next explosion of water from Old Isaac's blowhole. At the turtle farm they saw the crawls full of giant green turtles, one of the Cayman Islands' most famous features and export specialities, and Abelard insisted on presenting her with a carved turtleshell trinket holder.

'Souvenirs are part of the fun of new places,' he said when she thanked him, and looked pleased at her genuine pleasure in his gift.

She learned quite a lot about Abelard, his family and the company that day, and about Thea, and it came as a surprise to learn that Thea was British.

'Yes, my son spent three years in Britain and married a Scottish girl. Thea was born just up the road from you, in Edinburgh.'

Abby gave a little smile. To someone from the vast spaces of the States, Edinburgh could seem like 'just up the road' from the village in Northumbria were Abby was born.

In the newfound camaraderie she did not realise how much of herself Abelard had drawn from her, or that she had betrayed something of which she had only recently become agonisingly aware herself. So she experienced shock when Abelard stopped the car and stared reflectively at the sea as he said: 'Well, do you reckon Thea and K.B. will make a go of my company?'

'I—I can't answer that,' she said after a long hesitation. 'I'm only a secretary really.'

'Maybe. But you wouldn't be here unless you were important to K.B. Besides,' he turned those shrewd blue eyes on her, 'I've never underestimated the ideas of the folks on the sidelines. There's an old saying about onlookers seeing more of the game.'

'Yes, but . . .' Abby bit her lip, 'I don't have either the knowledge or the authority to make a valid assessment. I don't know all the facts, figures, all the pros and cons behind a deal like this one.'

'Facts. Figures.' His sharp gesture dismissed her

objections. 'Listen, honey, when the talkin's done and the money-wisin's spelled out it's still people who make the cogs fit.'

'Yes, but I thought . . .' Abby hesitated again. 'The question hardly arises, does it? I mean, Thea won't—she won't be with the company by then, if the deal goes through.'

'Oh, yes.' A rather strange little smile compressed his mouth. 'As you will know, I hold the controlling interest in Delicare. My son and my nephew held the bulk of the rest equally between them—at least they did until my son died. When he turned that damn auto over in Turin three years ago his holding passed to Thea. And she has no intention of ever letting go.'

There was a silence. Abby looked at the deepening gold of the westering sun and felt a chill settle within her. Abelard said flatly, 'This has been the trouble all along. She's always resented the fact that her cousin held an equal interest. And she's always resented not being allowed to develop her own ideas. Lee is pretty cautious. He looks after the pharmaceutical side—it's our safest and more profitable division. But Thea would channel everything into her new cosmetic project. Lee isn't in favour of the risk. Neither am I.'

'Balclairs are going to chance it,' said Abby, after a pause. 'Would it be such a risk for you?'

'Hell, yes! You've got to remember we started primarily as a small mail-order business. As such we had to play it cautious. All those folk in the Farm Belt, in Cotton Country, all depending on the catalog each season for their goods. We had to give them what they needed, and it hadn't to be too expensive—or too fancy. They trusted us. But now . . .' he shook his head, 'Thea would take us way, way up market. She really believes we could compete with Estee, and Arden, and Revlon.'

'She has confidence, and so has K.B.,' said Abby. 'What's wrong with that?'

'Nothing. But will they tear my company apart?' Abelard rested one arm across the wheel. 'I'm weary of the endless wrangles. Much as I love Thea—since she was a tiny kid she could play me her way—I don't want to see Delicare changed out of all recognition, or worse. More than that, I've a duty to all the folk who work for me. Some of them are like my own family. Their fathers worked with mine. And we owe them as much loyalty as they brought us through the years.'

The ring of total sincerity in his voice touched Abby. She said slowly, 'It's true that K.B. would make changes. He'd be the last person to pretend to you otherwise. But they'll be for the best, I'm sure.'

'You really think so?'

'Yes.'

He nodded, then turned his head to study her. 'You kinda like him, don't you, honey?'

Abby made no attempt to dissemble. 'Yes, but how did you guess? You've scarcely seen us together.'

'Your cheeks turn pink when you talk about him.' Abelard put his hand on her arm and smiled. 'It's a real pretty pink, honey.'

'Is it?' Abby felt the 'pretty pink' deepening into what must be a most unbecoming scarlet. With an urgent need to change the subject she looked up at the sky and observed, a little wildly, 'Goodness, isn't it getting dark quickly!'

'It does in the tropics. I guess we'd better get moving.' He reached for the starter, then checked for a moment. 'Thanks, honey.'

'What for?' she asked, with some surprise.

'For being a sounding board and giving me your day. I reckon it's done me good to talk it out with someone new.'

He put the car into motion and Abby subsided back, silent and with a warm sense of pleasure. All the love and all the loyalty in the world could not blind her to the difference in approach between Abelard and Kell Balclair. Maybe it wasn't fair to judge on one day of acquaintance, but she could not help wishing that her intractable boss would be a little more like this affable, companionable American. Somehow she just couldn't do anything right for K.B. . . .

This misgiving was not to be unfounded. Abelard managed to miss the villa and drove far past it through the darkness that increased the unfamiliarity of strange ground. They were back to the lights of George Town before they realised it, and with a rueful exclamation at his stupidity Abelard turned the car and set off once again.

The atmosphere was not a little strained when they walked in. Although Kell gave no indication of any annoyance when Abelard apologised, adding easily that time always seemed to fly when one was enjoying one-self, Thea made no effect to conceal her anger. It appeared she had had plans for the evening which were now ruined, and the icy glints of fury in the glare she directed at Abby left no doubt as to where the blame lay. Her grandfather was unperturbed.

'Well, why didn't you go ahead? You could have left a message and we'd have followed on. Hell, you know I don't care to dance, anyhow.'

Her mouth tightened and the toss of her flame-red hair as she turned almost threw sparks. She helped herself to a drink, and there was an uncomfortable silence for a few moments. Then Abelard said, 'Okay, the night's still young. Let's go some place. Wherever you like. I'll go and change.' With this he walked from the room, as though all were settled.

For a moment Abby thought Thea was going to indulge in tantrums and refuse to move, then with an ill-humoured shrug she flounced away to get ready.

Kell looked at Abby and her heart quailed. His eyes were so cold. But the feared retribution was not yet evident. He said in clipped tones: 'You'd better find Evalina. Tell her we're eating out. I told her to hold any preparations for the evening meal until you and Abelard got back.'

Abby licked dry lips. 'I'm sorry about that—if you were worried. But I——'

'Not now.' With only Mark still in the room it was painfully obvious that Kell was making no pretence at the charade he himself had instigated. 'I'll talk to you about that later.'

There was no doubt about his ominous tone, and no escape possible. Abby went to do as she was bid, then hurried to shower and change, scarcely stopping to take much care over her hair and make-up in case she was last and kept the others waiting. She was in deep enough as it was!

Despite her rush there was something extremely attractive and appealing about Abby when she snatched up her purse and almost ran along the corridor into the hall. The sun had kissed her fine skin with the first gilding of its golden glow and her feverish haste had added pink to her cheeks and brightness to her eyes. Her coral dress, of silky material that left one shoulder bare and swirled into very fine accordion pleats, was of a colour that she was happy in, and her waist was slimly cinched in a copper belt that matched dainty high-heeled evening sandals.

She skittered to a halt, realising the hall was empty and she need not have rushed. She took a sighing breath, oddly disconcerted, and moved slowly towards the outer door. It would be probably be quite a while before they all gathered; Thea certainly wouldn't hurry herself; her kind of presentation took time and she definitely belonged to the make-a-special-entrance-last brigade, Abby reflected cynically. For a moment she paused, hand on the door latch, and wondered if she should return to her room and make one or two more leisurely adjustments to her appearance, then her mouth hardened and she thrust at the door with an abrupt movement. Why try to make herself glamorous for a man? And why try to compete with the luscious Thea?

The night air was soft and warm yet refreshing against her heated skin and she passed through the soft pool of light falling from the patio lantern. Then she saw the blur of white in the darkness beyond and stopped, making to draw back at the same moment as an arm shot out and hard lean fingers closed round her wrist.

'Come to make your explanations?' Kell drew her inexorably along into the shadows of the garden.

Abby stiffened warily. 'They're hardly explanations. Mr Abelard wanted to explore. You'd all disappeared, so there was only me to entertain him.'

'So you took off for the better part of the day.'

Abby's mouth tightened. 'I seem to recall that I'm paid to do what I'm told. What was I supposed to do? Start telling him what to do when he said he wanted to see the island?'

'Okay, point taken. What did you talk about?'

Trying to stifle her resentment at his peremptory tone, Abby began to recount as much as she could remember of the conversation between herself and Abelard, leaving out the extraneous content and had gone indoors. She set down her glass and wondered uneasily if she should stay where she was—they'd probably be out any moment—or if she should go inside. Was she expected to welcome them? K.B. hadn't made that clear. But then, she reminded herself bitterly, she was still only an employee, not hostess to his host. And if she went rushing in it might be construed as curiosity. Whatever she did was bound to be wrong, Abby thought resignedly as she stood up and hesitated. She turned, and wasn't prepared for the vision emerging from the villa.

So this was Thea!

The newcomer was clad in dazzling white. Silky shirt carelessly knotted to bare a smooth tanned midriff and enhance shapely breasts, the tightest white pants Abby had ever seen—they were virtually a second skin—and a white plaited hairband from which glorious red-gold tresses rippled and cascaded over her shoulders.

Instantly Abby experienced a mind-picture of herself, garish, even, by some quirk of fancy, overdressed, in comparison to Thea's elegant simplicity. Kell was with her, and behind his tall form were two men, one young and fair-haired and of slight build, the other stocky, grey-headed and somewhat older than Mark.

Kell stepped on to the patio. 'Thea, meet Abby—my third hand.'

'Hello.' Thea flicked a not terribly interested glance over the younger girl, although it was not sufficiently uninterested to miss any details. Abby smiled tentatively, began to raise her right hand, then hastily let it fall to her side as Thea gave no indication of indulging in any formalities. Then Abby started inwardly and could not stop herself staring at the beautiful, self-possessed Thea with startled recognition. This was the trying to be succinct.

When she had finished there was a silence, an ominous silence.

'So,' Kell said at last, 'you discussed the whole business. You little fool! You let him ask questions. You even had the nerve to talk about my plans. My confidential business.' Low fury made every word bite. 'How dare you!'

'But I didn't!' She stared up into his angry face. 'You've got it all wrong! He wanted to talk things out. His own feelings about the company and the take-over. Get it straight in his own mind. Kell,' she said desperately, 'he didn't try to make me betray any confidences. I've told you! He didn't ask me lots of questions. Only if I thought you would make a lot of changes.'

'And what did you say?'

'That I thought you would. Kell! You're hurting me!' She put one hand to where his fingers clamped bruisingly into the soft flesh of her arm. 'What could I have done? If I'd refused to go with him he might have been offended. And I couldn't just clam up all the time.'

He released her arm. 'You should have sought one of us. Mark was in the house.'

'You should have thought of the possibility before you vanished,' she said bitterly. 'I suppose Thea had priority.'

'I can't afford to offend her—or the others—until everything's safely wrapped up.'

'Oh, yes! But when I use the same reasoning it's all wrong! Personally, I'd have thought that Abelard was the most important member of the party. But you know best!' Furious now, and uncaring of what she said, she glared up at him. 'Well, don't worry, sir! I'll take good care I don't say a word to anybody from now on. Just yes and no and thank you. Thank God I'll be out of it all by next weekend!'

She flung away from him, and was seized before she had taken two steps. The painful grip on her shoulders forced her to turn, and she stumbled, almost falling. The arm that saved her and yanked her against his hard body was anything but gentle. Holding her prisoner, his mouth a tight, relentless line, he stared down into her mutinous face.

'You're being silly now,' he said icily, 'and you seem to have forgotten something. We made an agreement.'

'Which I gave notice of ending.'

'Yes—in a way typical of a woman. But then I seem to remember you reneged on a previous agreement,' he said cruelly.

Her cheeks whitened, became so pale her skin gleamed silver under the moonlight. 'That wasn't an agreement. It——'

'I was under the impression it was—a business arrangement that differed in principle not one whit from any contract drawn up in cold print,' he told her scornfully.

'I wasn't the one who broke the rules of the contract that night,' she whispered bitterly. 'But I wouldn't expect *you* to understand. Not when you refused even to listen to——'

'Let's not start that argument again,' he broke in roughly. 'Just remember that I spelled out everything concerning this trip. You agreed to my terms. I expect you to abide by them.'

'You mean you want your pound of flesh!'

'No.' He was very close, so close she could feel the warmth of his breath on her cheek and smell the tangy fragrance of the aftershave he'd used. 'I mean there's no backing out.'

Without warning his mouth came down hard on her parted lips and the pressure of his body was so violent it crushed and hurt her breasts. There was no tenderness in him, only a deep simmering anger that matched her own, yet her traitor body sensors seethed into turbulent life, urging response. She did not hear the small exclamation a short distance away, nor sense the presence of an onlooker.

Kell's head lifted at last, leaving her mouth blurred and bruised from his possession of it, and his eyes glinted down into hers.

'Just remember,' he said in a dangerously quiet voice, 'I own you for two more weeks. And don't you dare try to forget it!'

CHAPTER SEVEN

IT was not an enchanted evening for Abby.

She was still disturbed and shaken when the party reached the hotel and she could not forget the expression on Thea's face during those moments when Kell released his dominant hold and she realised there was an onlooker.

Thea had looked startled, angry almost, as Abby swung round and saw her standing there in the moonlight, then the older girl had regained instant control. She had laughed. 'Last-minute business, Kell? Or do you just hate wasting time?'

He had made some easy reply, but Abby had gone scarlet with embarrassment. Mark and Lee came out at that moment, followed by Thea's grandfather, and there was a general movement toward the cars. Now, across the dining table with its glowing rose lamp and waxen blossom centrepiece, Abby surprised a speculative look in Thea's eyes. Thea held the glance deliberately before she looked away, and later, after a session on the dance floor, Abby saw that same look return. Anger simmered anew in her; how could Kell appear so infuriatingly calm and urbane, plainly expecting her to exhibit a display of *joie de vivre* while he took to the floor *three* times with Thea, and after his disgraceful behaviour before they set off? And why was he allowing Thea to give him the whole seductive treatment, looking as though he were enjoying every moment of it? After convincing her, Abby, that he was afraid of getting trapped!

'May I?'

Tall, mocking, Kell held out his hand to draw her on to the floor, and temper, disgust and hurt warred in Abby's heart. Pride longed to refuse, even as the shaming flare of excitement swamped all other emotion, and the glint in his eye dared her to snub his request.

'*Dance . . . in the old-fashioned way . . .*' he sang softly and lovingly into her ear, drawing her closely into his arms as they moved into the dancers.

'I'm not an old-fashioned girl,' she said bitterly, trying to separate herself from temptation. 'I'm just something you own for a couple of weeks, remember?'

'Nothing wrong with my memory,' he said coolly. 'I wish I could say the same for your acting.'

'If your memory is as good as you believe you'll remember I warned you about that very thing,' she flashed. 'And there's something else I should have warned you about, only I didn't foresee it,' she added with despair in her voice.

'Oh?'

'It doesn't work,' she said flatly. 'One minute you treat me like a pretend lover, and the next you come on the strong boss and expect me to jump to order.'

There was a thoughtful silence from him, then he said calmly, 'Yes, I'll have to do something about that.'

He did not seem inclined, however, to divulge whatever he might have in mind concerning this matter, and Abby could only wait and wonder in some trepidation as the evening at last dragged to its close.

The discoveries already made were quite enough to be going on with, she decided wearily when in the privacy of her bedroom she could let the mask of assumed gaiety slip as she sank into bed. Being in love was the most exhausting state she'd ever experienced; it was also the most ecstatic, miserable and frustrating plight imaginable. Useless to listen to the voice of logic telling her she'd get over it once she was out of his orbit—she didn't want ever to be out of his orbit. It was a painful truth, but impossible to deny; no matter how furious he made her, how furiously he treated her, it needed only a touch, only a glance, only a glimpse to set her heart pounding, her nerve ends jangling, and every sense yearning for a satisfaction only he could give. No man had ever had this effect on her before, and there was still a small stubborn corner of her mind that tried to cling to the immunity all but lost.

Wild notions of playing up to Lee came into her head, only to be dismissed as the foolish ideas they were. It hadn't taken long to discover that Lee was hopelessly in love with Thea; the expression in his eyes during unguarded looks at her was all too easily interpreted. So, was it so silly to endeavour to offer a measure of consolation? It was silly for two people to let their eyes betray their longing while Thea monopolised Kell's attention and Kell showed no apparent objection to this seductive brand of monopoly. But Abby knew she could never feign an interest she did not feel, other than normal friendliness, likeable and sociable as Lee was, nor did he in his turn evince any desire to make the best of the nearest girl available. He was basically too sincere, and so was Abby.

The next two days were almost unbearable.

Thea called the tune, and it seemed that now they must all dance. At the crack of dawn next morning a fishing trip began. Abby cried off this, and no one made much attempt to dissuade her. Secretly, and perversely hurting inside because Kell had accepted her demurring with seeming readiness, she resigned herself to a quiet day reading, swimming and sunbathing, only to be surprised by the party's return at noon, laden with the marine ingredients for at least three days' provender.

'The fish just about jump into the boat—I got three straight away!' Thea boasted. 'Who's going to dive the wall with me this afternoon?'

She had heard about the splendid facilities for diving offered by the islands and could not wait to start exploring some new underwater scenery.

So this had to be next on the agenda. The boat, gear and an expert guide were hired, and once again Abby was made aware that she seemed to have limitations— at least whenever Thea was around. Kell was an experienced swimmer and skin-diver and, predictably, Thea was an expert who had no intention of playing around in the shallows when all the sheer drop-offs that are an exciting feature of the reefs round the Caymanian ccoastline waited to be explored.

Mark and Lee contented themselves with a swim, then decided that going in search of a game of squash was more in their line, Abelard declined to be lured by the deep, and Abby was not even asked if she would like to essay a little underwater exploration.

Abelard, a faint gleam of sympathy in his eyes, took her for a game of tennis, which he blatantly let her win, and apologised for not being a better consolation prize. Abby was becoming used to his sudden dry little remarks and felt a twinge of guilt for not being a brighter companion, for she liked this kindly man very much and was beginning to wonder about two things. First, why Kell had not levelled straight away with Abelard instead of indulging in all the moves and ploys of business tactics, and secondly, how Abelard could have a granddaughter who seemed to have inherited neither his kindness nor his rugged charm. But already a pattern was forming, one that seemed to ensure that Thea enjoyed herself by simply getting all her own way, even if nothing else went according to plan.

Twenty-four hours later Thea was still enjoying herself—and having her own way, Abby reflected with a sigh, and it looked as though Kell wasn't exactly miserable as he caught the laughing Thea's hand and hauled her up beside him, where she curved her slim pliant body into the shape of his side and stretched out her free hand to catch spray.

They were climbing the famous waterfalls at Dunn's River, and Abby was still a little bemused at the speed with which a whim could transport six people. At breakfast that morning Thea had suddenly proposed a trip to Jamaica. Mark had murmured something about whether there were daily flights, and Thea had simply told Lee to ring the airport, and if no early scheduled flight then see if a charter plane could be got.

Lee went eagerly, wanting only to please her, and an hour later they were on their way. Thea had said airily to Abby: 'Pack for overnight—in case we stay,' and there was nothing to do but follow the instructions. For the first time Abby allowed a tinge of bitterness to creep into her thoughts. It didn't seem fair that one girl should have so much and possess so much power, able to indulge her slightest whim. And yet her jet-setting way of life seemed only to generate more restlessness and under the outward gaiety there was a suspicion of unhappiness, that Abby sensed. But it's nothing to do with me, Abby kept telling herself. She was simply an employee, here to do exactly as she was told—hadn't Kell spelled it all out with utter clarity? He *owned* her, he had said, for two more weeks.

She was forced to admit that in a material sense it was perfectly true. He was picking up the tab for every penny of the expenses, and she had agreed to his conditions of her own free will. But how could she have foreseen that somewhere along the way his pixilated plan would go haywire—and she would be foolish enough to lose her heart?

Well, the two weeks were already reduced to twelve days. Then she could start trying to forget Kell, and peace of mind might come back. And if Thea succeeded in capturing him he deserved all he got, Abby told herself. For once within her snare he would soon discover that Thea wouldn't stand any nonsense. This thought provided Abby with a certain perverted kind of satisfaction which, unfortunately, did not last long.

All through those days of sightseeing and watching Thea so close to Kell the anguish of truth persisted in homing to Abby's heart; no matter what he did or said, she wanted to be owned. Anything, even his arrogant, cavalier attitude, was preferable to being reduced to her present status of a mere presence who was the recipient only of an occasional casual remark.

When the party got back to the villa very late the following night Abby's memories of the places visited were all overlaid with mind pictures of Kell and Thea. They were ever present, even though the originals were out of sight, and they blotted out sleep during the dark hours, making her writhe and turn restlessly in the big wide bed while her tired eyes learned the shape of every item and every shadow in the dim room.

The moon was late now, sending slats of radiance through the blinds, and a fitful breeze sent the shadows of the palms wavering and receding on the wall by the far window which Abby had left uncurtained. It was nearing four when she fell at last into a troubled sleep, only to awake to darkness after what seemed only minutes. She lay wide-eyed, listening for a repeat of the sound she was sure had disturbed her, but the villa was silent. Even the breeze seemed to have stilled.

She wanted a drink now, something ice-cold, and cool water against her eyes to dispel the dry smart of sleeplessness, but she would not venture into the bathroom and risk disturbing Kell. With sudden decision she flung back the covers and donned a bikini and short towelling jacket. Making no sound, she stole along to the kitchen, found chilled fruit juice to slake her thirst, and quietly let herself out of the side door.

It wasn't long to dawn now, the brief transition from tropical velvet night to the pearl and apricot chiaroscuro of a new morn. She left her jacket on the sand, magically seeming to shed weariness with it, and trailed her toes through the shallow ripples at the sea's edge. It was strange and unreal to have the beach to herself, to kneel and splash, to slake her body much as she had gulped the icy drink, to try to catch a trail of phosphorescence, and then, suddenly spent, sit on the soft strand with arms huddled round her upraised knees as she stared into the dark veiled scene of sea and beach.

It was no use; she couldn't forget, and she had never felt so miserable in all her life. Her tightly compressed lips trembled, her throat constricted with a swell of ache and two hot stinging tears trembled on the brink of her eyelids, waiting there to trickle slowly down her cheeks when she couldn't hold back from blinking any longer. *Blast Kell!*

'What's the matter? Insomnia?'

Abby went rigid with shock. Lost in her cocoon of misery, she hadn't heard even the whisper of a movement approaching. Now she felt the faintest stirring of the air about her as Kell lowered himself to the sand at her side. His arm brushed her bare shoulder and her whole body contracted violently at the slight touch.

'Lost your voice as well as the sandman?'

'No, of course not!' The denial she wanted to sound crisp and snubbing came out ridiculously choked and unsteady. 'Something woke me up and I couldn't get back to sleep, so I thought I'd come down to the beach, that's all. Do I need your permission?' she added on a rising note of anger.

There was a small silence, then he said softly, 'Do I detect a trace of acerbity?'

'You can detect anything you like,' she said bitterly.

'Oh. Sulking.' He made it a statement.

'No, I'm not!' She started to scramble up and was brought down again in a distinctly ungainly fashion.

'Just a minute.' The steely fingers round her wrist did not relax. 'All right, you've had your revenge, Abby. Now it's my turn.'

'What do you mean?' She jerked back from him. 'I've had my revenge?'

'You heard.' His voice was cold. 'You deliberately opted out of everything these past few days. You've clung like a limpet to Abe. Why?'

'That's not true! I——'

'Isn't it? Now what's going on? Or does he fancy you?'

'What!' Tears and hysterical laughter warred in her at the mixture of suspicion and disfavour in Kell's tone. 'Don't be so stupid!' she snapped. 'Or perhaps you'd prefer me to be rude to the man, and then tag on to your cosy little twosome! Well, I never liked going anywhere where I wasn't invited.' She wrenched her arm free of him, only to be pinned back ruthlessly by a lightning movement of the same arm from which she'd escaped for less than a second.

'Listen,' he gritted, leaning over her, 'you'd better get this straight before you lash out with your own stupid little surmises. You refused to join the fishing trip of your own accord. And I purposely didn't suggest you come diving because I'd no idea of your prowess in that line—if you'd ever used an aqualung, or even a snorkel—and naturally you didn't choose to enlighten me thus. So I decided I'd better spare you the possible experience of looking a complete novice beside Thea's rather special style in the water. Or hadn't you gathered yet that she doesn't exactly have much patience with greenhorns?' he added grimly.

Abby stared mutely past the outline of his dark head, her mouth stubborn, and her eyes unhappy. It was galling to her pride to have to acknowledge the tumult his nearness was causing, and she was thankful that darkness still held sway to veil the thudding pulses which must surely be visible. She heard him take a soft intake of breath, then he said in a changed tone: 'If I seemed harsh the other night, I'm sorry.'

'Oh, don't mention it,' she said flatly. 'It's quite true, anyway.'

'Well then, why the persistent objections to me? At least you know I'm not going to ooze booze until you're fighting off drunken fumblings.'

A stab of pain bruised her emotions. Couldn't he ever forget the obnoxious Keighley man and stop reminding her of his true basic opinion of her? 'I still seem to be fighting off fumblings!' she cried, 'drunken or not.'

'No, Abby, that was part of our contract. And not by the remotest stretch of imagination can I consider myself in a similar class to your escort that night at the Hawaiian Lei.'

Abby looked at him. She could distinguish his

features now, and suddenly all her anger drained out of her. She wanted nothing more than to reach up her arms and capture that dark head. But pride was not yet overruled and she remained stubbornly uncommunicative.

But as though he had instantly divined her weakness he looked down closely into her averted face. A small sigh of exasperation escaped him. 'Listen, Abby, I suggest we try to be friends. I can't believe you wish us to be enemies.'

No, the cold little voice of reason said in her head, *he's only concerned with how he's going to be affected. Don't you realise that there's no such thing as friendship with a man like Kell? Only enmity—or love.*

She moved away abruptly, to sit in a huddled little position with her back to him and her head down, not trusting her reactions. 'No, of course I don't wish us to be enemies,' she said in a small voice.

'Good.'

She sensed him move and knew she too should move, because she no longer trusted herself when he touched her—and every woman-instinct she possessed told her he was going to touch her any moment now. Then the touch came, not like the cruel bite of steel but like the sensuous caress of velvet. And now it was too late.

'We'd better seal the pact, hadn't we?'

She was well aware that the 'hadn't we' paid only the merest lip service of rhetoric. He was kneeling behind her, one hand turning her chin to make her face him while his right arm drew her into the crook of his shoulder. The lovely tints of dayrise were stealing across the sky and the first rays of the sun behind the shoulders of the island were gilding the drifting night clouds. Abby exclaimed, 'It's light already. The——'

Kell's mouth stopped her speech. This kiss was strange. It was light and sensuous, different from the previous arrogant and bruising attacks from his mouth. It was dangerously disarming, and when he allowed their clinging lips to part she gave a small, uncertain smile. 'Well, pact sealed, sir?'

The unconvincing little attempt at a joke brought no response of amusement. He held her at arm's length now, considering her almost objectively, as though he were deliberating on the follow-up kiss; for certainly it was coming. Abby's heart pounded like that of a frightened bird. She didn't want to resist. She wanted to experience the hard pressure of his body against hers, compelling and intimate from tip to toe. But the obstinate streak of pride still held her back, still whispered the fear that such a surrender could only brand her as cheap. Because he'd made little secret of his opinion up till now, hadn't he?

His mouth lifted slightly at one side, then gently but irresistibly he eased her down on to the soft pillowing sand. There seemed no force about him now and she made an attempt at protest. 'Kell—it's day. They'll wonder—shouldn't we go back?'

'Do you want to go back?'

She looked up wordlessly into the darkly handsome features. A wicked hint of a smile flitted briefly across his lips and he shook his head. 'No—you can't fib your way out this time, my sweet.'

'What do you mean—fib?' She was suddenly breathless under the firm pressure of his hands, conscious of the strong tanned body communicating its proximity. One set of lean fingers fanned out on her shoulder, their featherlight touch drawing a collar of small circles round her throat. 'I—I don't tell fibs,' she whispered shakily.

'It would be a waste of time.' The fingertips traced the shape of her collarbone and the little angles it made, then trailed unashamedly down into the warm hollow between her breasts. They lingered there, brought to a halt by the line of her bikini top, and seemed to consider taking steps to surmount the obstacle. 'The vibes are too strong,' he added coolly.'

'What vibes?' Abby brought her hand up to parry the exploring one.

He trapped her hand instantly. 'Aren't you receiving any?'

She let her eyelids droop, as though the frail defence would hide the betrayal in her eyes. She knew she should escape before she lost her wits entirely and snatched at fools' gold. 'I thought it was the echo of the sea,' she said as airily as she could, and began to slide out from his grasp.

But the movement only allowed his arms to pass under her body. 'You talk too much,' he murmured just before the warm hard pressure of his mouth found hers.

It was impossible to prevent the shudder of response that rippled through her body. As though he felt it, Kell's arms tightened and his lips moved demandingly over the soft outline of hers until almost unwillingly she gave a tiny sigh that was near despair and let him part her mouth to take sweet deep possession.

The sand beneath her no longer held the night's coolness. It burned against her skin, matching the heat his long hard torso generated in her body. His caresses smoothed like silk, moulding her even closer, sensuously awakening desire in a way infinitely more dangerous than his previous lovemaking when anger had spurred passion.

Abby lost count of time and conscious action. Of

their own accord her arms had found their way about his broad muscled shoulders and her whole body seemed to have melded into one aching, burning entity of desire. She was returning his kisses now, revelling in the feel of his skin under her mouth, tasting the male tang of him and sharing the air of his breath.

Suddenly, in a voice blurred against her throat, he whispered, 'Why aren't you always like this?'

'Why aren't you?' she breathed.

'I am.'

'You're not!'

'I think you mistook my meaning.' He took her lower lip between his own in a teasing love-play that silenced her and brought response leaping like a flame in her. His caresses were becoming more urgent, and she knew that she wanted him to go on caressing her in this magic shell of pleasure, yet when his hand slid down her body, explored the warm satiny mound of her tummy, she stiffened and murmured unsteadily.

The caress stilled. 'Is it taboo to touch you there?'

'You know it is.' The old inhibitions made her turn her face away, chased all the lovely joy and began to chill her flesh.

'Taboos are made to be broken—sometimes.'

'Not now.' She was breathless, suddenly as angry with herself as with him. 'Don't try to make me, Kell.'

'Don't you trust me?'

'It's not that—I'm not ready. I——' Her voice broke thinly as she glimpsed a movement beyond his shoulder. 'There's Thea! She's *watching* us!'

'So what?' With total calm Kell remained unmoving, looking down into Abby's unhappy face with dark, enigmatic eyes. His arm stayed across her body, keeping her his prisoner. 'They say eavesdroppers never hear any good of themselves—we may as well give an eaveswatcher something to watch.'

'*No!* she's coming along.' Abby evaded the embrace he seemed to have every intention of resuming and sat up, feverishly adjusting the bra top he'd disarranged and pushing back the tangles of hair from her brow. From the corner of her eye she saw Thea's tall svelte figure undulating along the beach towards them and sheer hatred burned in Abby's heart. Why couldn't Thea give her a chance?

Kell was looking over his shoulder and his mouth had compressed. But he stayed where he was, his long form half lying, half sitting, looking perfectly nonchalant, considering he had just been forced to desist from his efforts to break down Abby's inhibitions.

Poor Abby was far from such admirable self-possession. She wanted to get up and run, but a warning pressure from Kell's hand stayed her. Thea halted and looked down at the couple on the sand, and a malicious amusement flitted over her face.

'Don't look so embarrassed, darling,' she said to Abby. 'We all have these little capers occasionally. Nobody takes them seriously.'

Abby felt her body going scarlet from head to toe. She looked round desperately to see where her jacket had got to when Kell slipped it away from her shoulders those momentous aeons ago. It was lying only a little distance away, wrinkled and sand-folded, but before she could make the movement to retrieve it her wrist was seized and Kell was pulling her upright. The next moment sea and sky spun wildly as he swung her up into his arms and ran down the beach to splash into the sea.

The warmth of his chest was against her face, the sight of Thea was cut off, and she was too surprised to struggle. Then Kell was plunging deeply into the crystal water, taking her down with him, and the immersion was driving all breath from her lungs. She gasped as her head broke the surface, gasped again as Kell lunged for her. 'What did you do that for?'

'Do what?' He put his hands on her shoulders with the obvious intention of ducking her again.

'This!' she exclaimed breathlessly.

'It seemed the obvious way of cooling unrequited passions. Unless you've any better idea.'

The swell carried her against him, and the surge of the sea became an ally one moment, an enemy the next, bringing them together, then parting, until Abby could not resist both the sea and Kell. Holding her in his crook of one arm, he trod water and said in a voice that sounded unsteady for him, 'That was a very convincing act! You very nearly convinced me!'

The spell was broken at last.

Abby plunged away from the compelling power of his body, a power which held a compulsive magnetism at any time but which had become unbelievably sensual when experienced within the surging element of the sea. Heedless of whether he followed or not she struck out towards the shore and the villa, and now tears were mixing with sea spray to make rainbow prisms across her vision.

Of course it was all just an act. How could she be so foolish as ever to forget it? Even though in her opinion it was a stupid, pointless act and she still couldn't fathom why he had ever insisted on her playing along. If he treated Thea's feelings the way he treated hers he wouldn't have much to worry about. But of course he had to be nice to Thea, until his plans for his company's expansion were successfully completed.

Abby felt beach underfoot and stood up, to stumble through the shallow ripples. She let the tears run unchecked now, not bothering to dash them away as she blindly realised that for once nobody would know she was crying.

Thea was lounging on the terrace, still clad in the long, diaphanous silk caftan that had doubtless been the only reason for her not taking to the water after Kell, Abby thought bitterly. The seductive lines of Thea's shapely body were plainly quite naked beneath the luminous colours, and she looked far more desirable in the full-length veiling than Abby felt in her brief bikini as she dripped her way across the terrace.

'Here.' Kell had caught up with her. He had snatched up her forgotten beach jacket and he now slung it roughly round her shoulders. His tone sounded as curt as the movement had been, and Abby murmured a choked acknowledgment as she hurried indoors, not needing to look back to know that Kell had stopped to dally with the glamorous redhead.

By the time she had showered and dressed and partaken of a sparse breakfast Abby was beginning to feel the reaction from a sleepless night and the onslaught on her emotional system wreaked by Kell's lovemaking. If only Kell meant it all! And if only she still didn't feel so bound by the inhibitions of a kind but fairly strict upbringing. For she knew quite well where Kell's lovemaking and her own longing for him must lead if left unchecked, and she knew she was not yet ready to take that final step into womanhood, not without love and total commitment to make the trinity of the man—woman relationship.

She was brought out of her reflections by Abelard remarking on how pale she looked. He sounded concerned, and the genuine care in the older man's expression brought the smart to her eyes again. For the first time since her childhood Abby felt the longing for the father she could only just remember. With fathers one didn't have to pretend. They provided the shoulder and the special comforting understanding that even a mother could not always supply.

She murmured a conventional response, then caught the unsympathetic grin flitting over Thea's face.

'Pace a little too fast for you, honey?' enquired the redhead.

Before Abby could frame a response that was suitably put-downing without being noticeably rude Abelard shot a sharp glance at his granddaughter, then leaned his elbows on the table and smiled at Abby. 'I guess this cosy little island doesn't lend itself to a good long drive, but there's a period house I'd like to take a closer look at in town. Like to come along, then we'll have a lazy meal some place?'

Abby did not hesitate. It was just what she needed to escape from a somewhat overcharged emotional state. 'Thank you, I'd love to,' she exclaimed. 'What time do you want to——'

But before she could finish Kell broke in smoothly: 'Would you mind . . .' he looked at the older man. 'I'd like to discuss one or two points today, if it's okay with you, Abe?'

The older man shrugged. 'That's what we're here for. Sorry, Abby,' he gave her a wry smile,' another day, maybe?'

'Of course. Do you need any particular notes?' she asked Kell, unconsciously falling back into the formal employer–employee relationship.

'No, I won't need you today, you can amuse yourself,' he told her in a tone that made a mockery of his lovemaking so short a time ago.

He went off in search of Mark, saying they would talk in the big sitting-room at the front of the villa,

and Abelard said there were a couple of calls he wanted
Lee to see to for him. Abby and Thea were left in
silence at the dining table.

'I suppose I'd better change and go and sit in on
this discussion,' Thea grumbled, shaking her head at
little Sarah who had skipped excitedly into the dining
room to ask if anything else was required.

Abby smiled at the little girl, who was immaculate
and dainty in a sugar-pink crisp gingham dress. 'You
do look pretty today, poppet. Mind you're not late for
school.'

'I'm going now.' With a swish of her skirts Sarah
darted away, and Abby hurriedly gulped down the rest
of her coffee. Evalina would be wanting to get cleared
away.

Thea stood up. 'Are the shops any good here?' she
asked abruptly.

'I haven't explored them yet. There doesn't seem to
have been time,' Abby returned, also standing up and
aware suddenly of Thea's penetrating stare. That same
searching look with a hint of puzzlement that she'd
turned on Abby the day she arrived. Then suddenly it
cleared and Thea gave a small exclamation of satisfaction.

'Of course!' she said slowly. 'Now I remember. I
knew I'd seen you before. It was in London. The night
Kell took us to that Hawaiian place.' Thea's expression
hardened. 'You were the girl involved with that ghastly
heavy. And Kell, naturally, had to play the cavalry.'

Abby's heart chilled with despair. Were the conse-
quences of that night never to end? She'd simply tried
to do a good turn for a friend and look where it landed
her. And was it so awful, after all? Other people did far
worse things and nobody took any notice. But the
Hawaiian Lei was an expensive, sophisticated res-

taurant; diners behaved themselves: they did not get involved in unpleasant scenes with disreputable-looking drunks like Jack Keighley.

'I suppose you know you wrecked our evening,' Thea said coldly.

'It wasn't intentional,' Abby said wearily, 'and I'm sorry, if that will be any recompense.'

Unexpectedly Thea grinned. 'It's over, why worry? Now I know you were just one of those escort girls I reckon you'll be wise enough not to get any kinda silly ideas about Kell.'

'What do you mean?' Abby's eyes widened.

'What I say. He's a terrific man. But because he happens to want——' Thea paused and gave a delicate shrug '——you know what I mean——'

'A bed partner?' Abby said through tight lips.

'You said it, honey.' Thea moved towards the door. 'But men like Kell don't marry their bed partners.' With this parting stab she opened the door, only to turn back, a somewhat unexpectedly friendly look softening the approach. 'Feel like coming for a saunter round the shops?'

Abby scarcely hid her surprise. Then she shook her head. 'No, thanks—I'd better stay. I'm a bit tired anyway.'

'I'm not surprised!' observed Thea with a meaning lift of her brows. 'See you, then.'

She departed with her usual nonchalance, leaving Abby right down to nadir, reflecting wryly that she had certainly left herself wide open to that little parting salvo.

The villa seemed very quiet after Thea had gone. There was only the murmur of the men's voices, muted by the closed door, and the faint chinking sounds of dishes coming from the kitchen where Evalina was no doubt working away at her task of keeping the villa routine running so smoothly.

Abby felt useless. She wandered out into the garden, looked at the blazing colours of a screen of flowering shrubs and tried to identify them, but without success. It was another gorgeous day, the sun riding high in its incandescent splendour, the sea a sparkling milky jade at the rippling edge of the beach and deepening to sapphire crystal farther out, but none of nature's bounty could lift Abby's spirits. Although Kell had dismissed her for the day she still hoped that something might crop up and he might call her in; even work would be preferable to lolling around in her own miserable company.

She selected a paperback from a row on the shelf in the lounge and went outside again to settle herself in a shaded corner of the terrace. But half an hour later and about fifty pages on she let the book close and slide from her hand, knowing she had retained scarcely an inkling of what she had read. Her mind persisted in dwelling on one man only, and the immutable fact that her happiness revolved round him alone.

It wasn't fair! A word, a look, a smile, a frown could make or mar her day. And the effect he had on her physical senses made her painfully aware she no longer had total control over her own body. She closed her eyes, fighting the temptation to allow memory and imagination to return to the dawn hour, even though she knew the foolishness of it. Because she meant nothing to him, nothing permanent, certainly not love in the way she had always dreamed love should be. Why, she moaned softly to herself, for her first time of being really in love, did her heart have to fix on an ambitious, irresistible axe-grinder like Kell Balclair?

Impatient with herself and her daydreams, she got

up to move after her shade, which had left her as the sun moved higher. About to settle down, she thought she heard a phone ringing indoors and paused to listen. It continued, somehow conveying an urgency, and when it seemed that nobody was going to answer it she hurried indoors and picked up the receiver.

The voice on the line was male, terse and urgent, and as she listened Abby's face puckered with concern. 'Yes,' she responded quickly, 'I'll give him the message immediately. But wouldn't you like to speak to——'

'I can't tell him anything else,' the voice interrupted. 'Just tell him I think he should get here right away.'

The line clicked into silence and Abby stared at the receiver for an instant, then thrust it back into place and ran along the hall to the sitting room door. She burst into the room and looked through the haze of cigar smoke to where Abelard sat. Heedless of the abrupt cessation of discussion and Kell's startled exclamation from the other side of the room, she said gently, 'Your personal secretary has just called from your home. Please try not to be too alarmed, but your wife isn't very well. They were worried about her, and the doctor decided to get her into hospital. Your secretary knew you'd want to be told and that you'd want to go to her straight away.'

Abelard started up, his face pinched and greying with shock. 'But what happened? What's the matter? Why didn't he——?'

'I wanted to bring you to the phone, but there are no details yet about her condition. It seemed she had a bad night and considerable pain. They only took her to hospital ten minutes ago.'

'She was fine last night when I called her.' Abelard passed his hand across his brow, and Abby noticed the fine mist of perspiration breaking on it. She said hurriedly, 'I'll get you a drink. It's been a shock . . .'

But Kell had already forestalled her and was holding out a glass. Lee said, 'Try not to worry, sir. I'll go and check the plane times.'

A little colour came back into the older man's cheeks as he sipped the reviving brandy. Abby looked down at him with anxiety and sympathy in her heart, sorry that she had had to be the bearer of bad news. Abelard glanced up at Kell. 'Sorry to have to break things up, just as we were seeing daylight. But I have to go to my wife.'

'Of course,' Kell said soothingly. 'And if there's anything at all we can do . . .'

Lee rushed back into the room. 'Sir, we're in luck! If we can make it to the airport in time. But we've only got twenty minutes.'

'That'll be long enough.' Abelard got up. 'Go and pack.' At the door he stopped and exclaimed, 'Where's Thea?'

He groaned when Abby told him. 'She could be away all day. How do we find her?'

'Don't worry.' Kell touched the older man's shoulder. 'You and Lee get to the airport. I'll look after Thea.'

CHAPTER EIGHT

As if Thea needed looking after!

Abby shivered in anticipation of the cold, depressing London drizzle that awaited her emergence from the car and reluctantly opened the car door. It exactly matched her homecoming spirits.

Mark got her cases out of the boot and set them down outside the flat, then turned up his jacket collar and grinned down at her.

'Cheer up! It was nice while it lasted.'

'Yes,' she said, without conviction. 'Thank you for driving me home, Mark.'

'A pleasure. Sure you won't change your mind and come back for a meal with us? My wife would be very cross if she thought you were taking pot luck by yourself.'

Abby shook her head. 'You're very kind, but I'm not really hungry and it's so late.'

'Okay, in you go and I'll bring your luggage and see you safely in.'

The flat was in its normal state of chaos when she entered, and not for the first time she felt ashamed of the lackadaisical homemaking efforts of her flatmates. She stood unhappily while Mark carried in her cases, then said goodnight and watched wistfully as he went out to his car. He would have a well-ordered home run to a well-ordered routine; she could not imagine Mark living in any other setting. The idea began to seem very attractive all of a sudden. It was all very well to have the fun of a place of one's own, to do as one liked and sling possessions around without a parent to read the riot act about untidiness, but somehow there was something lacking once the novelty wore off. Abby brewed herself a cup of the old familiar one-bag variety and viewed the depressing little sitting-room with disfavour. Some day she would choose furnishings in cane, natural, with very pale green carpet and ceiling the same colour, and one wall a deep green and the others paler, with masses of huge plants against one wall, a place that would be totally relaxing after work, and she'd learn to cook seafood and make exotic desserts . . .

You're getting stupid ideas, she told herself furiously. She'd be getting broody next! And that was the height of foolishness, she thought bitterly. For the cause of all these wayward daydreams could hardly be termed the settling-down steady type. Oh, hell! she muttered under her breath, and went to start unpacking, wishing that somebody would come home and relieve the loneliness.

But nobody came that night. Dorice was on a few days' holiday, Suzanne had been sent on a Paris job, and nobody had expected Abby back for another week, she was informed by Emma when that aspiring young actress arrived home the next evening, after two days in Manchester on a special promotion for somebody's new shampoo at a trade fair. Emma was in high good humour because she had landed a part in a new television serial that was due to go into production later in the year. Meanwhile, she had to eat, hence the shampoo.

Abby herself was to become painfully aware of this vital matter during the following weeks. Her first day back at work was disturbing by its sheer negative quality. Kell was not back, there was nothing for Abby to do, and Betsy had not wasted opportunity as it knocked during Abby's absence.

Betsy had dug herself in very comfortably, complete with her personal battalion of greenery stationed along the windowsills and atop the filing cabinets. Abby's delicate little fern had been relegated to an obscure corner where it languished sadly in the shadow of a vigorously spreading philodendron.

Abby gave it a much-needed drink, determinedly replaced it where it ought to be, and pondered on her plan of action. Short of removing Betsy by forcible methods, there seemed no way Abby could repossess her domain, and adding the fact of Kell's absence, plus her own decision to give him her notice, there seemed little point in trying to formulate any plans.

It was Betsy who was given the message that said Kell would not be back for at least a week, possibly ten days. And it was Betsy who continued to deal with all incoming mail and saw to the letters that went to Kell's deputy for attention. Abby spent three miserable days, trying to fill her time, hating every moment that brought the end of the week nearer. What should she do?

It was only there, in the office where she had worked for and with him, that reality closed in relentlessly. It was hopeless to pretend otherwise. She had told him she was leaving; she had advised him in a somewhat forceful manner to find himself another secretary. And he had made it quite plain that he understood; he owned her service for two more weeks. No matter that he'd made love to her; he'd never pretended that it was for any other reason than a purely business affair. She'd be the silliest of fools if she tried to kid herself that there had been an iota of personal feeling for her on his side. For even foolishness could not close her

memory to that last sight of Kell at Owen Roberts
Airport.

Kell's dark head beside the red-gold beauty of Thea's.
Kell seeing to her luggage, helping her out of the car in
that superbly courteous way of his that made you forget
the curter moments. Then escorting her aboard the plane
after a few last-minute directions to Mark, and turning
for only a brief, cursory farewell of Abby.

Thea had won after all, despite Kell's avowed efforts
at ensuring she stayed at arm's length. At the last
minute it seemed as though fate had played into her
hands and brought the man she wanted within her
reach, willingly. And who could blame any man for
surrendering, for Thea was lovely, intelligent, witty
and honest about what she wanted from life, even if
she didn't have much time for her own sex.

Goodbye, Kell, my heart, Abby whispered sound-
lessly. When he came back he wouldn't expect to find
her still there. Any speculation on his possible reaction to that eventuality was enough to make Abby
shrivel inside. He would either laugh, or scorn her, or
be angry, or, worst of all, dismiss her with that icy
disapprobation that went straight to her heart like a
rapier. No, she had to make the break; she couldn't
bear to risk it.

She went to see the personnel manager, now ensconced in his tastefully fitted new office. Mr Anthony
Drew looked at her with vague puzzlement, as though
he tried to recall exactly who she was, until he located
the appropriate pigeonhole in his memory and smiled
a friendly welcome.

'What can I do for you today?'

Trying to frame the words she had rehearsed in her
mind, Abby could only look at him and wonder how
she had ever imagined herself in love with *him*. The

carefully dressed blond hair looked artificial in its apparent casualness, there was hardness behind the smile and a hint of calculation about the eyes. The whole added up to a self-satisfied, handsome young man who sat snug and smug in the niche he had carved for himself.

The amusement continued to linger round his mouth as Abby explained haltingly, trying not to give away too many details of the circumstances during which she had given notice. It wasn't very easy, and she had a suspicion that Anthony Drew was filling in the blanks quite easily—and filling in a few that hadn't actually existed. His brows went up when she finished.

'Well, that was a silly thing to do, dear, wasn't it?'

There was no doubt that Mr Drew knew his way round employee's silly little ways. If she agreed meekly with his observation she admitted foolishness, albeit to the extent of playing the fool with the managing director, of all people, and if she denied it she would still look an idiot, only a stubborn one instead.

Her resolution hardened. 'I thought it was routine—and courtesy—to let you know.'

'Oh, so you aren't having second thoughts? You don't want me to intercede on your behalf when K.B. gets back? Blame it on the tropic of old Capricorn or whatever tropic it is?'

'No, thank you,' she said tonelessly.

Apparently losing interest in her, he scribbled something on a pad in front of him and reached out his other hand to the phone. 'Okay, we'll take it from last week, when you tell me you informed K.B. of your wish to leave. I'll inform Pay and Records. Sorry you haven't been happy with us,' he added perfunctorily.

And that was the end of it.

On the following Friday Abby's cards and final

salary were ready for her, and Betsy's smile seemed more smug and knowing than ever, even though Abby had told no one except Mr Drew. She supposed it would have gone round the grapevine pretty quickly, not because she had made any great personal impression on Balclairs during her working spell there but because of the reflected glory—if that was the right term for it, she wondered bitterly—of being P.S. to the M.D.

It was a strange sensation to walk out of the office for the last time, and know that she had turned the knife herself. She would never see Kell again . . .

Emma thought she was crazy, and said so in no uncertain terms. 'God, you're a fool! A plum job like that. Why, Abby? *Why?*'

'Because I don't want to work there any more.'

'Because you don't . . .' Emma's eyes were sharp and very shrewd. 'That's no answer. Sure you don't mean you don't want to work for *him* any more?'

Abby turned away. It was not easy to hide anything from Emma, and to be truthful there was only one thing—other than Kell—that she wanted now, and that was a sympathetic ear. Gradually, the confidences came. 'I—I just couldn't face him,' she said miserably.

'Yes, I can see why,' Emma's mouth pursed. 'You've really fallen for him, haven't you? Never mind, you've done the right thing,' she said briskly. 'It'll hurt like hell for a few weeks, then you'll start forgetting him.'

'Will I?' Abby couldn't remotely envisage this ever happening.

'Of course!' A hint of admiration made Emma's expression serious. 'I didn't think you'd have had the courage, though. Some girls hang on, even when they know it's hopeless and they haven't a chance. But they can't bear to make the break, and they look so pathetic, waiting for the slightest crumb to fall. All the same,' Emma shook her head, 'It's a shame about the job. You might find it's a long time before you land such a good one again.'

'I found that one, I'll find another,' said Abby with the confidence of one who had not yet known failure. She felt a little better having told somebody, but knew in her heart a full understanding of what it meant to be waiting for the crumbs. She would never know now if he succeeded in capturing the American company, or settled for a merger. How was Abelard's wife? Was she recovering? And Thea. Would Kell marry her?

This last question was never far from Abby's mind during the miserable weeks that followed. She wove wishful fantasies in which she walked into a coffee bar and saw him there, or bumped into him as he was getting out of his car, or saw him at an art exhibition she visited. But the fantasies remained exactly that, pure wishful thinking. Kell was gone, as though he never existed, as though she had never stepped into his world for a few brief, tumultuous months she would remember till the end of her life.

But gradually other worries became more insistent. Contrary to her expectations she did not succeed in getting another job. The country's economy was hitting one of its periodic slumps and the supply of jobs, recently so plentiful, at least in the secretarial department, was drying up. Abby wrote applications, tramped from one place to the next, lowered her sights to more humble levels, and still failed. And of course she had come away from Balclairs without a most important thing; a reference. But she would starve rather than go back and beg for this. A crumb?

Her small savings began to diminish at frightening speed. What was she going to do when they'd gone?

Admit defeat and go back home to Grandmother Gabrielle? There would be no 'I-told-you-so' reminders; Grandmother Gabrielle was too kind and understanding for that. But it still didn't make it any easier to give up the London dream.

Abby, never chubby, began to lose weight and the attractive country roses that Mr Drew had once complimented her on. When Emma tentatively suggested an escort double-date at very short notice one day, assuring her that she need have no qualms about taking it on, Abby agreed with an alacrity that would have astonished herself six months earlier.

The men were a couple of young Canadians, and they were such cheerful company Abby almost enjoyed herself, despite her now inevitable searching glance for the sight of a certain dark head.

When the girls got back to the flat Emma said triumphantly: 'There! That actually cheered you up! Now you've realised you're not automatically going headlong to the devil!'

'There's a letter behind the door.' Abby groped down in the dim light. 'No, it isn't—it's a note for you to ring somebody.'

Emma glanced carelessly at the scribbled, unsigned message, her mind still on her diatribe. 'I mean, life isn't all weighted against a girl, you know. Young men find themselves alone in the city, on business maybe, and don't know anybody. But if they don't watch out they find they've been ripped off in some sleazy joint.'

Abby could see the truth of this, but it would be a long time before she forgot Jack Keighley.

'Jake is very particular about his escort girls,' Emma went on. 'I wouldn't be one of his spare-timers if he wasn't.'

'Well, that's next week's rent safe,' said Abby.

thankfully, making her way towards her room.

Emma was following her, a flash of concern crossing her face. 'Don't rely on this happening very often, Abby,' she warned. 'It's a nice little bonus, but that's all. It may be weeks before another job turns up.'

Abby stepped out of her dress and hung it up. 'I've two interviews tomorrow. I'm sure to get one of them. By the law of averages there's got to be a door opening soon.'

'Sure. Don't get low, whatever you do,' soothed Emma.

'No—it's only my bank balance that's sinking,' Abby returned with a desperate attempt at levity.

But it looked as though her depleted bank balance was in danger of drowning by that weekend. She had not succeeded in winning any of the several jobs she had sought that week, and the law of averages seemed to be defying all computed reputation as far as the numerical odds in favour of a door of opportunity opening for Abby were concerned. When her grand-mother telephoned on the Saturday night she caught Abby in a very dispirited mood indeed, and the threatening tears Abby tried to suppress could not be disguised, even by telephonic communication, from Grandmother Gabrielle's astute intuition.

'Why don't you forget about this career business? Come back home where you belong. We've all missed you so much.'

The familiar homely voice brought a surge of nostalgia, but Abby said stubbornly, 'I can't, Gran. If I give up when it gets a bit difficult I'm admitting failure.'

'Rubbish! Sometimes the right job takes a bit of finding. I still don't quite understand why you left Balclairs, it seemed such a plum, but I've got my sus-

picions. If I'm right, I'm very glad you did leave, be
cause it means you haven't let London go to your hea
and make you behave in a way you might regret late
on. Not that London has an exclusive claim on im
morality,' the older woman added dryly.

Abby hovered between tears and laughte
Grandmother Gabrielle sounded so Victorian as sh
made those statements, yet in reality she was far fron
being a strict, prudish upholder of moral sanctity. Ha
she been, she would never have let Abby cut free o
the apron strings so easily.

Abruptly she changed the subject. 'I saw old M
Wade the other day and he was saying how much h
misses you, Abby. It seems he got a new woman in
but she hadn't a clue. Then she went off and foun
herself a job in a little drapery. Said she liked chattin
to the customers about their knitting patterns.'

Abby closed her eyes. Could that be the height o
ambition? Not that there was anything wrong in knit
ting, but what about living?

'Poor Mr Wade's books are in an awful state,
Abby's grandmother went on. 'He said he was in
terrible mix-up with his Value Added Tax. He'd wel
come you back with open arms,' she added somewha
graphically. 'Why don't you think it over, darling?
mean, you don't have to come back for ever. There'
no knowing what might come along for you. But i
would help you get over this sticky patch you seem t
be in.'

Go back and sort out Mr Wade's V.A.T.? All thos
stacks of stark new timber, the funny little hut an
the vintage typewriting machine ... The prospec
appalled, yet there was something about the tug o
home roots that might help her get over this heart
breaking yearning for a man she could never have. A

long as she was still here, knowing he was in the same city, she was going to cling to the fragile straw of hope, hoping to glimpse him one day . . .

Pouncing unerringly on the moment of weakening, Grandmother Gabrielle said firmly: 'Now stop fretting. I'm going to put your train fare in the post first thing Monday morning. Then there's nothing to stop you being home by next weekend. You can have a nice little holiday while you decide what you're going to do next. Now give my love to Suzanne—she's never in when I ring. 'Night, darling.' She rang off before Abby had time to make further argument.

The promised cheque arrived promptly by the Tuesday morning post. Abby propped it against the cereal packet and stared at it with desolate eyes. She might as well go back. The fates seemed to be conspiring to that end. Last night Suzanne had wanted to know if Abby had definitely made up her mind to leave. It seemed a friend was coming to London and looking for somewhere to live. Suzanne was very keen to have her friend move into the flat, so it would all work out very conveniently.

Suddenly Abby made up her mind. She looked across the table to Suzanne. 'Your friend can move in whenever she likes. I'll clear out my stuff today and leave tomorrow morning.'

She felt a strange sense of fatality as soon as she had spoken, almost as though a weight had been lifted from her, yet the emptiness that was left was numbing. She picked up the cheque and letter and stood up, anxious now only to have done with it all. She met Emma's startled glance from the doorway.

'What did I hear?' Emma's eyes had lost their morning languour instantly. 'Did I dream it, or did you say you were going?'

'You're not dreaming,' Abby said flatly. She mad
to brush past Emma's slender form, not wanting t
talk about the end of all her dreams and plans, bu
Emma barred her way.

'Hey! You can't go tomorrow!'

'Why not?'

'There's a special job on. It should have been las
week, but there was a mix-up.' Emma looked worried
'You've got to be here tomorrow.'

'Why me? And this is the first you've said about
or any mix-up.' Abby looked puzzled for a momen
'You said I hadn't to count on it very often.'

'I know!' Emma shook her head wildly. 'But the
asked specially for us.'

'Who did?'

'Those two Canadians.' Emma caught her arm. 'Abby
you must stay—make it a farewell party if nothing else
One more day won't make any difference.'

'No, I suppose not.' Already it seemed like a re
prieve, and when Emma suddenly wailed how much
she was going to miss Abby the temptation to go bac
on her decision was very strong. But nothing would b
resolved if she did; her problems were only liable t
get worse.

The hours of reprieve seemed to fly. Abby started t
sort through her personal possessions, a task she di
with reluctance, and was surprised at the number o
things she had acquired during her sojourn in the flat
It was even more surprising how attractive the flat'
once despised untidiness now seemed as she was o
the point of bidding it goodbye. She packed everythin
except for the clothes she would need and various bit
and pieces she bestowed on Emma. All that was neede
was to decide what she would wear for her last evenin
in London.

She had worn her blue velvet skirt and silvery top the previous week; it was a noticeable rig-out, so she packed it carefully as she did not want to wear the same things again. Beside it she laid the coral creation that brought back such shattering memories of a moonlit garden in the Caribbean. She could not bear the thought of wearing it for anyone except . . . Only the lemon jersey silk remained. She would have to settle for it, although for some unaccountable reason she had never felt quite happy in it, even though it had seemed so attractive when she chose it. A bad buy, she reflected, shrugging her shoulders. Still, what did it matter how she felt for this particular occasion?

Emma, however, decided it mattered a great deal.

'You look terrible,' she said with total bluntness.

'Well, thanks!' Abby's expression tightened mutinously. 'At least how I look will match how I feel.'

'Sweetie, it isn't just that.' Emma waved her hands. 'We all make these mistakes sometimes; buy something that looks gorgeous in the shop when we try it on, then suddenly we find it was all a mirage. But it's the colour! Your tan's fading, and you looked washed out.' Emma walked round Abby, her eyes critical. She shook her head. 'It just hangs on you as well, like a clothespeg. You can't wear it, Abby.'

Abby argued, determined not to unpack her case, and Emma said impatiently, 'You know I've told you about the place where I get my clothes. They're all couturier models that have only been used for display or modelled a couple of times. I offered to take you along and introduce you.'

'So that I too could have a wardrobe like yours,' said Abby with a sigh as Emma flung open the doors of her enormous wardrobe.

She was going to miss the fun of these trying-on
sessions, Abby thought as she watched Emma riffle
along the rail of glamorous creations in a rainbow of
colours, and miss the make-up swapping, the experi-
ments with new ideas, the confidences and the glimpse
into the fascinating world of showbiz that Emma
supplied. But even that would have ended soon, Abby
knew, because Emma was going to be out of London
for some time when the new production got under way,
and afterwards Emma was hoping to find a place of
her own, or one shared with only one other person.
Painfully, Abby was discovering how quickly life
moved and changed, and that it only stored up sadness
for oneself not to remember this. To break the unsettl-
ing chain of thought she asked Emma what she planned
to wear.

'This! Isn't it gorgeous?' Emma drew forth a floating
swirl of deepest black with glints of silver shimmering
within its folds. She hooked it on the top of the cup-
board and reached for a dark blue dress. 'Try this. It
doesn't look much on the hanger, but it's stunning
on.'

But not on Abby, unfortunately. It made her look
just as wan as the lemon silk. After a couple more 'try
ons' Emma frowned worriedly. 'You look more lovelorn than ever!'

'I can't help being pale!'

'Rubbish! You've let yourself be possessed by that
macho industrialist. Forget him!'

'What do you think I'm trying to do?'

Emma sighed. 'I know. The trouble is, you need a
man to make you glow.'

'And now the candle's blown out! You do have ways
of giving out confidence!'

'Sorry!' Emma giggled. 'But you've got to have

colour—and make-up won't do it all. Why not wear your lovely copper and coral?'

'No way. Anyhow, I just spent an hour packing it in tissue paper.'

'Well, I guess it'll have to be this.' Emma returned to her rummaging, muttering under her breath, 'I don't know what you're going to do without me to keep sorting you out. Here—I've wanted to give you this for some time, but I thought I'd better let your happy memories of Jack Keighley fade a bit first.'

Emma was holding out the beautiful rose dress. She said impatiently, 'Well, take it! It's made for you. I shall never wear it again. But it is an original. Please, Abby, I'd like you to have it.'

With mixed emotions warring in her, Abby took the dress from Emma's outstretched hand and murmured her thanks. It did have unhappy memories, yet it was true that its lovely clinging lines and glowing colour suited her as though it had been designed with only her in mind. Her wan little face took on an ethereal quality, her eyes seemed to darken, and the skill of the couturier's art transformed the slender lines of her body into seductive shapeliness.

Kell had remembered this dress ... which only proves that men remember the clothes, not the girl inside, she told herself bitterly.

There was no more time for agonising over Kell— she had done more than enough of that already. Just let this evening get over quickly; eight o'clock tomorrow morning would see her on the train for the North. She'd find a job, save some money, then come back next year to try again, a little older, a little wiser, she hoped.

'Did you put any scent on?'

'No, I forgot.'

'Trust you! Yes—it does matter!' Emma exclaimed, beginning to hunt in her purse. 'Keep still, for goodness' sake!'

'Where on earth are we going?' demanded Abby when the taxi disgorged her and Emma in a cloud of Yves Saint Laurent's Opium. She peered suspiciously into the stygian, unsalubrious-looking depths of a narrow lane.

'The taxi can't go down here—it's only a few steps,' said Emma, taking Abby's arm. 'It's a new club. I thought those two nice Canucks would enjoy it. Wonder if they're here yet.'

A black cavern in the wall, with a single light above, was the entrance. Inside a dimly lit flight of steps curved down into the bowels of Soho. In a small lobby, where obviously a considerable economy drive on electricity was still in force, Abby looked at the green and black lipstick on two girls waiting there, and the scarlet suit of a young man with silvery hair the same colour as his face, and wondered what Emma had got her into this time. There was the thump and throb of reggae coming from regions as yet unseen, and a man in black with very strange eyes was brushing past her, pausing to light a cigarette in a long green holder before he crossed the lobby. The whole atmosphere was decidedly sinister, and Abby's imagination began to work overtime; even Jack Keighley began to seem healthily normal in retrospect.

Emma opened one of the three doors leading from the lobby and peered through. A surge of smoke laden heat and the whine of the synthesiser welled out into the lobby, bringing with it a not easily definable undertone of something rather sickly and alien to Abby's nostrils. She rushed to Emma. 'Can you smell that?' she whispered. 'Is it marijuana?'

'Could be.' Emma seemed less concerned about this possibility than something else that had brought a narrowing to her fine brows. 'I wonder where . . .'

She was interrupted by a curt voice demanding that the door be shut immediately, and Abby said unhappily, 'I'm sure we've come to the wrong place, Em. Let's . . .'

'No, you haven't come to the wrong place,' said a voice behind her, a dry voice that was all too familiar.

Abby whirled round, disbelieving, her eyes widening with shock. It couldn't be! It couldn't be Kell!

CHAPTER NINE

HE stood there, taller and more good-looking than ever in this weirdo place, immaculate as only he could be in black velvet evening jacket, dark slim trousers, a dark rose shirt ruffled discreetly and perfectly fixed bow.

Abby's heart did parabola leaps that came up into her throat and threatened to render her breathless. 'W-what are you doing here?' she stammered.

'Looking for my escort,' he said dryly.

Dickie Tennent stood a little way behind him, raising one hand in a salute of recognition. Kell turned and formally introduced him to Emma. Speechlessly, Abby watched. Emma and Kell seemed to know one another. It all seemed to have been arranged. Suddenly Abby found her voice.

'I don't understand,' she cried to Emma. 'You said we were meeting the Canadians. Why didn't you——?'

Emma was laughing. Kell took Abby's arm. 'There's been a slight change of plan,' he told her smoothly. 'It happens all the time these days.' He glanced at Dickie and Emma. 'Have a good time, you two—and thanks, Emma.'

They were turning away and starting up the steps that led to the exit. Abby came out of her trance.

'Just a minute!' She tried to shake Kell's hand off her arm. She glared at him. 'I'm not staying here with you!'

'Neither of us is staying here,' he told her coolly, apparently unaffected by her indignation. 'You're coming to dine with me.'

'I most certainly am not!' she retorted. 'I don't work for you now. You can't order me about any more.'

'I'm not disputing that,' he returned coldly. 'However, as at least one man I know of, and seemingly one certain Canadian, have been allowed to buy your company for the evening, why am I discriminated against?'

'My company isn't for sale to you!'

Suddenly he seemed to lose patience. He released her arm and turned away. 'Okay. If you're determined to stay here by yourself, then stay.'

His long legs were taking him up the steps two at a time, and several pairs of curious eyes were watching Abby. With equal abruptness Abby realised she certainly did not want to be left there to make her way home alone. She rushed after him, almost stumbling in her haste and just remembering in time to pick up her long skirt before she tripped up the steps. He was waiting at the top. Without speaking, he took her arm and guided her the short distance along the dank and scary alleyway. His car was parked at the corner. He unlocked the front passenger door and thrust her inside.

When he slid behind the wheel he turned to her before he switched on the ignition. 'Please try not to argue, Abby. I'd prefer to make the journey in silence, but if you must talk will you try to do so like any ordinary human being. You know, little pleasantries about the weather, or the present state of the economy.'

'Yes, but——'

'I know.' He sighed and pressed the starter. 'I have to admit the scheme's misfired. But then all my schemes seem to misfire where you're concerned.'

Abby's mouth opened, then closed. She couldn't see

him in the darkness, not enough to read his expression, but his tone was warning enough. He would answer no questions before he was ready.

'That's right,' he said dryly, 'just sit and worry about it.'

Abby gave a sigh of repressed fury. How was he always able to read her mind? Yes, her mind was worrying round a dozen questions, and she knew perfectly well that he was quite capable of adding a few more to the list before they reached whatever destination he had in mind. *Was he going to ask her to come back to Balclairs?* But he would have sent her a letter, not let all this time elapse. Could he have discovered that she was a more efficient secretary than she'd realised? *But it wasn't fair!* After all it had cost her to break away. And now, thanks to the scheme that had misfired, whatever it was, she was back, caught fast in the spell, more aware than ever before of his nearness, the spicy tang of the aftershave he used, the outline of his dark head, the light glinting on the dark hair on his wrist as he swung the wheel; she was parched for the whole indefinable magnetism that radiated from him.

Abby put her hand to her throat and turned her burning face to the window. Where were they going, anyway? He was travelling southward and she vaguely recalled that they had crossed the river miles back. Suddenly something snapped in her spirit and all resistance vanished. She reclined back with a sigh into the sweet leathery opulence of the big car. Control of her immediate destiny had been snatched from her again—had she ever regained it?—and she might as well be honest and admit that for the moment she no longer cared . . .

The car was travelling fast now and the city left

behind. Huddles of lights twinkled past, dim landmarks she did not recognise, and the traffic had thinned. She stole a glance at her watch; an hour had gone already. Where was Kell taking her?

She had her answer a little while later when he left the main highway and drove along a quiet road that wound through the Kent countryside. He seemed to know his route, choosing turnings without hesitation, until he slowed to pass through a wide gateway and took the incline of a curving carriage driveway with smooth ease. Abby glimpsed the dark outline of a country house with tall chimneys silhouetted against the night sky. Dark patches of vine clung to its walls, and big mullioned windows caught glinting reflections of the car's headlights as it swept to a halt on a gravelled forecourt. It all looked very quiet and deserted for a hotel! Especially as there wasn't a light to be seen apart from the two old lanterns at either side of the entrance.

She knew that he was going to draw keys from his pocket to unlock the heavy oaken door, knew that this was his home, and that strange eternal old instinct of feminine intuition told her why she was here.

He had probably had many women—was she the first not to fall into his arms with eager assent?—and for some reason she held a certain physical attraction for him. She would have to be stupid not to have realised this very soon in their relationship. Had the fact that she had resisted challenged his male ego, annoyed him because he'd failed to get her into his bed? Shivers of fear, anticipation, desire and despair chased each other down her spine, and she scarcely took in anything of the exquisitely furnished and warmly welcoming interior of the gracious old period house.

He turned to take her wrap, his expression unsmiling. 'I promised you dinner, Abby, but we'll have to get it ourselves.'

She stood there, small and oddly defenceless in the big panelled hall with its broad staircase leading up to a galleried landing. 'I can cook,' she said flatly, 'though I don't usually don evening wear in the kitchen.'

One corner of his mouth compressed. 'The kitchen's along here.' He led the way, his footsteps ringing hard and decisively on the polished parquet as he crossed the hall.

The kitchen was huge, the old brickwork and timber still preserved and the modern units carefully chosen to blend unobtrusively. There was a large old country-style table in the centre, and an array of various culinary utensils and ingredients laid out neatly. Abby looked round for something in the apron line to guard her dress, but the only thing that seemed to answer was a very new-looking plastic affair in butcher-blue stripes with a message in scarlet emblazoned across the front: *For the man who has everything!*

'May I?' She held it out.

'Of course. I have to keep it on show or Julie will be very hurt.'

'Julie?' Suddenly Abby's fingers refused to cope with the strings she was tying behind her waist.

'My housekeeper's daughter. She presented me with it last Christmas.'

'Oh.' Abby's fingers went on struggling. So even his housekeeper's daughter wasn't immune. She also, apparently had the entrée to his private office line. Abby straightened the glossy plastic stiffness and said, 'What's to be done?'

'There's side salad in the crisper drawer of the fridge. Can you make some dressing while I do the steaks?'

In silence she followed his directions and some thirty minutes later they were sitting down in the shadowy dining room. The table was already laid with silver and fine cut glass; obviously someone had done a great deal of preparation towards the meal. The St Julien was at just the right temperature, and the sparkling Moselle refreshingly misty cool. But although the food and wine and the setting could not be faulted Abby was ill at ease. He was not making it easy for her, and his cool formality made conversation very constrained. At last, as one of the periods of silence seemed to be getting uncomfortably long, she asked if the deal had been satisfactorily concluded.

'Yes. We've merged, and Abelard is going to retire at the end of the year.'

'How is his wife?' Abby asked, looking down at her glass.

'Much better.' There was no more information forthcoming. Kell's eyes seemed to be concentrating on her, searching her features and suddenly making her aware of herself in the rose softness of her gown. Nervously her fingers went to touch the small carved rose quartz pendant that fell just above the shadowy cleft between her breasts. As though the movement were a signal, Kell crumpled his table napkin. 'The coffee should be ready—we'll have it in the sitting room.'

At any other time Abby would have liked to look at the fascinating treasures the sitting room held. Lovely old pieces from a bygone age, their walnut or rosewood surface glowing softly with the patina of years of devoted polishing. He had mixed styles, both in the furniture and the pictures and bric-à-brac in the room, obviously choosing things he liked rather than seeking for a perfectly matched all-round effect. And they existed happily side by side, a dainty walnut bureau, a satinwood side table, Chinese flower prints and some Georgian silver beside a Swiss musical box inlaid with mother-of-pearl.

There were books too, shelves of them, but Abby went straight to the fireside chair and composed herself under the amber radiance of a tall floor lamp. Kell did not immediately sit down. He stood by the fireside, one arm resting on the mantelpiece, and stared reflectively into the flickering glow of the fire he had just switched on.

The room was quite warm, but the red glow gave a warmth of another kind, a sensuous witchery that brought Abby to fresh awareness of Kell's strength and her own weakness. His hands were so well shaped, and the stark black contrast of jacket cuff enhanced their masculine shape. He moved, and the movement brought the fine material of his trousers taut against his thigh. Abby set down her coffee cup with a trembling hand. 'I——' she began.

'Yes, it's time you gave me an explanation,' he said coldly.

'Me?' The time-capsule of warmth burst. She stared up at him. 'I don't owe you any explanation. I'm not your employee now! But you certainly owe me one. How long have you known Emma? Why did you—get her to work this up—set me up? If you wanted to see me why didn't you ask me? Instead of all this—subterfuge? It's——'

He held up his hand. 'Would you have come if I had?'

'No! Yes—n-no! Oh, I don't know,' she cried wildly. 'Stop answering my questions with new ones!'

'Why did you walk out before I got back from the States?'

She stared. 'But you knew I was leaving. I told you!'

'Did you?'

'You know I did!' She held her head for an instant, wondering if she were going mad. 'Twice!'

'I thought it was one of those heat-of-the-moment things we all fire off at times.'

'Well, it wasn't! Anyway, that was weeks ago. After you'd reminded me in your charming gentle way that you still owned me for another two weeks. Or was that just one of *your* heat-of-the-moment sayings?' she added bitterly.

His brows went up. 'Did I hurt you?'

'I'm not going to give you the satisfaction of knowing that. Oh, Kell,' her shoulders drooped tiredly, 'what do you want of me? Why bring me here?'

He straightened. 'To find out something.'

She shook her head. 'I don't understand you.'

'Don't you? I should have thought it was the simplest thing in the world.' He looked down at her, a slight lift at the corners of his mouth making him look cynical. 'I wanted to sort out my own feelings—and see if I could make you admit yours.'

'What?'

'Oh, for God's sake, Abby! Have I ever pretended? You attract me. You always have—ever since that first night I saw you with that drunken oaf. I could have felled him that night, to make sure he kept his lecherous paws off you.' Kell took a deep angry breath. 'And I wanted to thrash you in the car when I took you home, to knock some sense into your naïve young head.'

The sound of his voice seemed to go on inside her head, echoing and receding, while she could only stare at his dark, furious expression.

'He went on in a low, vehement tone: 'I've known
lot of ladies—again, I won't pretend otherwise—bu
never have I known one as infuriating as you!'

Abby had half risen from her chair. 'If I infuriat
you so much I fail to see where the attraction come
in. From the start you treated me like——'

'And then the next time I saw you Dickie was o
the scene—or you were! To be exact, virtually in h
arms,' he said, as though she hadn't spoken.

'You ought to know Dickie by now,' she shot bac
at him. 'He's one of your employees. It took me abou
three minutes—which you happened to choose to——

There was a sharp, determined rap on the door.

Abby froze with shock, while Kell muttere
something under his breath. Then his expression wa
controlled and his voice smooth with courtesy. 'Com
in,' he called, and re-assumed his nonchalant stance b
the fire.

The door swung open and a child stood on th
threshold.

She looked about eight, thin and freckled, wit
flaxen hair cut short about her small head. Her jean
were elaborately patched and her red checked shir
much too large for her. She gave an engaging grin an
said confidently: 'I've come for the coffee cups if you'r
finished. I've done the dishes and everything's read
upstairs.'

Apparently unaware of the effect of her advent, sh
marched across the room, gathered up the cups an
marched blithely back to the door. There, she turne
with another grin. 'If you want anything else, Mr K
just holler! Mum's watching that spooky thing on telly
'Night!'

'Thanks, Julie. Goodnight.'

The spell had broken again and Abby didn't know

whether to laugh or cry at the anticlimax. She looked at her watch, then at Kell. 'How am I supposed to get home tonight?'

'You're not.'

'I can't stay here! I—I'm getting the eight o'clock——'

He was shaking his head. 'You're staying here. Julie's probably popped her old cuddly rabbit into your bed just in case you're lonely in a strange room.'

Abby closed her eyes. 'She does this for all your guests?'

'Oh, yes.' His face was expressionless. 'Not that they all appreciate it, mind.'

Abby sighed. She could imagine this if his guests were of the sophisticated genre like Thea. Without thinking, she said, 'So that's Julie.'

His lids flickered. 'Why do you say that?'

'No reason.'

'Then why the note of relief?'

Abby looked away, her face flooding with colour. Was there no way of hiding anything from this man? He said slowly, 'Ah, yes, I remember. You must have taken the call the day she rang in a panic because Mrs Lake—her mother— had scalded herself badly. Did you wonder who Julie was?'

'It wasn't for me to wonder anything,' Abby said stiffly. 'As your secretary I did what I was told.'

'Yes. But you're not my secretary now.' Suddenly he reached out and grasped her arm. 'For God's sake, Abby, come where you belong and stop tormenting me.'

By the time the words were spoken he had his arms round her, enfolding her closely against the long hard length of him. 'Look at me,' he demanded against the top of the head pressed into his shoulder. Almost de-

spairingly, knowing she could resist no longer, s
raised her head and looked up at him. The moment
waiting for his mouth was a sweet agony, and at t
merging of their lips a shudder trembled through h
making a further meld with the tremor that shook h
body.

Her arms went round him, fingers interlacing
his dark thick hair, while heart and pulses hammered
swelling surge of need. His hands were hungry, seekin
every line and curve of her body, finding the swe
warmth of her breast and the instant response of desi
hardening to his fingerplay.

Lost in his kiss, she felt him draw the shoulder
her gown away, felt the shivering ecstasy of his tou
on her skin, then his mouth tease where his touch ha
played.

She knew she was dangerously near the point of r
return, and the message of his body warned that co
trol was all but gone. Yet even though the longing th
urged her to give and take the fulfilment every sen
craved there was a sadness, another longing that wou
never be granted. When he raised his head and sl
saw his eyes darkened with need his mouth move
roughly over her eyes and cheek and stilled against t
drenching moisture of her tears.

'Abby—what is it?' he murmured thickly.

'Nothing. It's—I——' blindly she thrust her fa
into his shoulder, trying to stop the foolish tears.

'But tell me! What is it?' he repeated.

She shook her head. 'I'm sorry, but I can't help i
she sobbed. 'This is why I ran away. Because I—
couldn't stop wanting you and——'

'But *I* want you just as much. I thought you kne
that.'

'I know, but I couldn't fight you any more and——

'But *why* do you have to fight me this way? I want you, my darling Abby. I want——'

'I know.' She raised a woebegone face and stared up at him. 'But I didn't want you this way. Not just to be another in the succession of girls like Thea who love you but can't keep you. I wanted all of you, just for me.'

'But you've got me! Abby, I *love* you!'

'No, you don't,' she said miserably. 'You want to make love to me. There's a difference.'

'Yes, I'm well aware of that. Just as I'm well aware of how you feel about me.' He cupped his hands round her small unhappy face. 'Maybe this will disillusion you, but it's a fact of life. You have to accept that I didn't get to thirty-four—and a position of holding certain power—without meeting a few lovely ladies and learning a bit about how they react to men. I could have seduced you quite easily. But——'

'Oh, no!' She leaned back from him. 'I never had the remotest intention of letting you seduce me.'

His mouth twisted. 'I never tried, my sweet, so don't be so sure.'

He never tried!

Wordlessly, she searched his dark features, seeing the faint lights of mockery in his eyes and experiencing the pain of the disillusion against which he had warned her.

'It didn't seem fair,' he said slowly, 'because as I got to know you I gradually became aware of how misleading was the situation in which we first met. Even so, I would still have doubts sometimes. I knew you wanted my lovemaking, but there was a barrier I couldn't get past.'

He paused, his eyes reflective. 'You know, Abby, that a girl's eyes usually betray her, betray her experience, even though her mouth looks soft and innocent

and her manner demure. But it's still possible to
misled. The most innocent-looking, misty-eyed you
Delilah I ever knew hid a heart of steel and the avar
of a Shylock under that unassuming exterior.'

'You don't think . . .?' With horror Abby instan
remembered all the expensive clothes for th
Caribbean trip. 'Those things you bought me . . .
was worried at the time about——'

'No, my conscientious little love, that's the last thi
I'm thinking of!' With a gesture he dismissed the sm
alarmed protest. 'No, my worry was the dawning rea
isation that you really were different. I hadn't the hea
to try to seduce you. And I knew the echoes in t
distance had to be wedding bells, and I certainly wasn
ready to start ringing *those!*'

The chill gathered round her heart and she look
away. He was only being honest—and she was grate
for that—and telling her what she had known
along.

He went on slowly, 'But when I got back from t
States, the satisfaction of the deal settled at last, I kn
something was missing from my life. Everything w
so damn flat! You'd got away from me, and by the en
of the first month I knew what was really the matt
with me. I wanted you more than I ever wanted an
woman in my life, and I knew it wasn't going to be t
kind of affair that fades away as soon as the next pret
lady happens along. I had to see you again and sort
out.'

He sighed, and looked straight at her with a lo
that melted her bones. 'Isn't anyone ever at home
your flat? I rang three times, no answer. Then I r
membered Emma, and that day I saw the pair of yo
near the Planetarium. I suddenly got this idea of turi
ing the clock back full circle and substituting myse

for that drunken date of yours that first night. I left a note for Emma, not putting my name in case you saw it, and banking on the fact that her way of life wouldn't cause her to question an unsigned note asking her to ring a strange number.'

'No, it wouldn't,' said Abby unsteadily, wondering how long she could resist going back into his arms. 'Emma thrives on situations like that.'

'She did ring, we arranged to meet, and she agreed to help me. In fact,' he smiled, 'she elaborated on the idea. That's how we finished up at that kinky dive, which apparently is one of her favourite haunts where she meets her pals from the theatrical fraternity.'

He was silent a moment, then, as though reading the unspoken plea in her eyes, pulled her roughly into his arms. 'I know you're young, and I know now that this is your first affair, and I don't want to rush you, but I want you so much. Oh, God!' he groaned, 'how I want you.'

The warm skin of his jaw pressed hard against her face and she felt the thud of his heart against her breast. She put her arms round him, knowing that it was time to make her decision. It was time to grow up. Time to forget about those fairy-tale endings and living happily ever after. She loved and wanted Kell so much she didn't think she could live without him. Even if the affair didn't last she would at least have had the joy of loving him, of giving and sharing their love. Without that she would have only the sorrow and emptiness of a future without him, a future in which she would never have known the supreme fulfilment of belonging to him.

'Kell,' she whispered.

'Yes?' He sounded a little weary.

Now she had made the decision she was uncertain

how to word it. She whispered, 'I—I've made up my mind. I—I don't know how to say this, but if—if you still want me I love you and I—I would like to——'

Tension had gradually been increasing in him as the halting little admissions came forth. 'Yes,' he said softly, 'you would like ... what would you like, Abby?'

'To—to live with you. Or love you.'

'*Come live with me and be my love* ...' There was a tremor going through him that was different, more like laughter than passion. 'Abby, my infuriating little love, I'm proposing to marry you, not make you my mistress. I want small, infuriating children who look like you. I want to come home to you at the end of the day, to someone who loves me for myself, who needs me to make their world precious, and who hasn't forgotten what the simple pleasures of life are. You're real and sincere and honest, my darling, and I love you more than I ever imagined a man could love a woman.'

'Kell—say that again,' she exclaimed wildly. 'I think I'm dreaming!'

'No repeats! There are other ways—better ways of telling you—and teaching you!'

Joyous laughter bubbled up in Abby—she had suddenly remembered a prophecy made many months ago by the worldly-wise Emma. What had she said? '*... some heavenly man is going to fall for your innocence like a load of bricks and spend nights of bliss teaching you what it's all about ...*'

'What's so funny?' he demanded. 'I'm trying to kiss you!'

She told him, helpless now with the sheer happiness of loving. 'I can't help it. I'm so happy.' And now she had no inhibitions about revealing her feelings for him. Long ages later, breathless in his arms and her face brilliantly flushed, she looked up at him with feverishly starry eyes, still not sure that it wasn't all a dream. 'How did we get down here?'

'Don't ask me.' He eased himself up off the soft white fleece of the fireside rug and drew her up with him on to the settee. There he straightened the now disarranged silk evening shirt for whose unbuttoned and crumpled state she apparently was responsible. But the message in his eyes totally contradicted the teasing reprimand on his lips.

She sighed against him. 'Tell me something, Kell . . .'

'If I can.'

'Why were you so angry and awful on the island?'

'Don't you know?'

'Would I ask if I did?'

'No imagination?' He teased the lobe of her ear with his mouth. 'But perhaps feminine imagination isn't quite capable of realising just how shattering it is for a man to start making love to a woman he wants and then have to turn back half way.' He paused. 'Question answered?'

She traced the line of his lower lip with a fingertip. 'Received and processing.'

'You've a lot to atone for!'

'I know—and I'm going to be made to atone for it.' She smoothed back her hair, then suddenly gave a stifled squeal.

'What's the matter now?'

'Look at the time! How am I going to get back tonight?'

'*I'm* not driving back to town tonight.' He buried his mouth in her throat and uttered a sigh that seemed to underline his immediate intentions quite clearly. 'You can forget about that, my darling.'

'Yes, but I've no night things if I stay here. Nothing.'

'I think I've a spare toothbrush somewhere. What else do you want?' he asked wickedly.

'To know what I'm supposed to change into tomorrow morning. How am I going to look arriving in London in an evening dress?' she demanded, laughing helplessly.

He pulled her close against him, effectively stifling any further argument. 'It's all happened before, my love, and it'll all happen again. Old London will never notice.'

'Our neighbours will!'

'You talk too much. This is much more important . . .'

Surrendering to his impatience, living her wildest dreams at last, Abby agreed. *This* was all that mattered!

A WORD ABOUT THE AUTHOR

Margery Hilton's background is in the performing arts. Before writing full-time, she ran a small dance school and later performed in musicals and pantomimes in England and Scotland. After marriage to the stage manager of her hometown theater, she worked backstage as props manager.

While she had never planned to be a writer, she had always longed for a typewriter of her own—just as a means to express her thoughts on certain subjects. When it arrived as a Christmas surprise from her husband, she decided to try her hand at a full-length romance novel.

During the months that followed, her story began to take shape, but it was shelved partway through because of an illness in the family. Some time later, the author herself suffered a back injury that forced her to give up her dance classes and theater work; she took her manuscript off the shelf and got back to work. "It saved my sanity," she says. Typing it took six weeks, and then, in a "rush of optimism," she sent it off to Mills & Boon, Harlequin's sister company.

It wasn't long before Margery learned that her manuscript had been accepted. *Young Ellis* (#1022), her first Harlequin Romance, was released in 1966; eight years later saw the publication of her first Harlequin Presents, *A Man without Mercy* (#52).